Translating the Bible

Choosing and Using an English Version

R T France

Rector of Wentnor, Diocese of Hereford
Formerly Principal of Wycliffe Hall, Oxford

Additional Chapter by

Philip Jenson

Lecturer in Old Testament, Trinity College, Bristol

GROVE BOOKS LIMITED
RIDLEY HALL RD CAMBRIDGE CB3 9HU

Contents

Acknowledgements

The bulk of the material in this booklet was originally written for a chapter in *The Oxford Guide to English Literature in Translation* (due to be published in 1999), though it has been adapted considerably. I am grateful to Oxford University Press for giving permission for it to published in this form.

The Cover Illustration is by Peter Ashton

First Impression March 1997
ISSN 1365-490X
ISBN 1 85174 338 3

1
Introduction

What is known as 'The Bible' is in fact a library of religious writings spanning a period of more than a thousand years, representing a wide variety of cultural contexts and of literary genres, and originating in three languages, Hebrew, Aramaic, and Greek. The collection provides the basic canon of sacred writings of the Judaeo-Christian tradition.

Its major component is the Hebrew Bible, comprising twenty-four books of varying length (subdivided in our English Bibles into thirty-nine). Substantial parts of two of these books (Daniel 2.4–7.28; Ezra 4.8–6.18; 7.12–26) and one isolated verse in another (Jeremiah 10.11) are in Aramaic, the rest in Hebrew. (Christians habitually refer to these books as the 'Old Testament,' but for Jews this term is not acceptable since it implies a Christian 'takeover' of the Hebrew Bible as merely an introduction to their own Scriptures.)

The 'New Testament' consists of twenty-seven Christian writings of the first century AD, written in the common Greek of the period, though with a variety of styles and levels of linguistic sophistication.

Translation of the various writings which comprise the Bible is significantly affected by their status as 'Scripture.' They thus constitute a canon of authoritative writings regarded by members of the Jewish and Christian religions as in a different category from other literature and, despite their manifestly human authorship, as conveying in some sense the 'Word of God.' Other Hebrew and Greek writings from the Jewish world and from early Christianity, while they may be valued for their literary and religious qualities, are not 'Scripture.'

There are, however, certain Jewish writings (of later date than the Old Testament books) which, while never part of the Hebrew Bible, were particularly valued in some early Christian circles. These are known as the 'Apocrypha,' and are included in some English translations of the Bible. These books were preserved in Greek, not in Hebrew, even though many of them came from Hebrew or Aramaic originals. Their status is defined in Catholic theology as 'deutero-canonical' (i.e. authoritative on a lower level than that of the canonical books of the Old Testament). Protestants generally treat them as of less importance: the Anglican Thirty-Nine Articles declare that 'the Church doth read [them] for example of life and instruction of manners; but yet doth it not apply them to establish any doctrine.'

2
Bible Translation before Translation into English

Translations of the Hebrew Scriptures became necessary by the third century BC, when many Jews no longer understood Hebrew. Translation into Greek (the 'lingua franca'—common language—of the Eastern Mediterranean) was focused in the large Jewish community of Alexandria. At first there were various individual translations, but by the end of the second century BC a standard collection, known as the **Septuagint** (signified by 'LXX'), was widely accepted. It was the Septuagint which was in effect the Bible of the first Christians, and which is copiously quoted in the New Testament. It is not the product of a single translation project, and the styles adopted for the various books differ considerably, some of them departing quite freely from the Hebrew text as we know it. Different manuscripts of the Septuagint witness also to considerable variations in the accepted Greek text. Later Greek versions of the Hebrew Bible were essentially revisions of the Septuagint, notably those of Aquila (a very much more literal version), Symmachus and Theodotion, all from the second century AD.

In Palestine and further east Aramaic was the prevalent language among Jews, and a variety of Aramaic versions of the Hebrew Bible, known as **Targums**, were produced around the same period. Translation of both Hebrew Bible and New Testament into Latin began very early in the Christian era. Towards the end of the fourth century Jerome was commissioned by Pope Damasus to produce a standard Latin version of the whole Bible, the **Vulgate**, which became the accepted text of the Latin church, so that relatively few manuscripts of earlier Latin versions survive.

Translations were also made in the early centuries into Syriac and Coptic (directly from the Greek) and 'secondary versions' translated from an earlier translation into Gothic, Armenian, Ethiopic and Georgian.

The character of these various early translations varied considerably. While some were the work of scholars such as Jerome, with a formidable knowledge of relevant languages, most were not associated with any named translator. The motive for their production was in most cases not literary so much as religious, to make the sacred texts accessible to worshippers who did not know the original languages. The written Aramaic targums, for instance, developed from the practice in the synagogue of giving an oral, probably extempore, Aramaic interpretation after the Hebrew text had been read.

Such versions are not likely to be marked by word-for-word accuracy, and the character of many of the surviving versions from the Septuagint onwards indicates that this was not always the primary concern of the anonymous translators. It is thus to be expected that a secondary version will be still further from the original. This was to be a significant factor when the Bible began to be translated into English, since it was Latin rather than Greek which dominated Western Europe, while Hebrew was little known among European Christians of the late Middle Ages.

3
The Problem of Textual Transmission

To return to 'the original text' is, however, no easy matter when we are dealing with ancient texts passed on in manuscript form before the days of printing. As manuscripts were copied in different parts of the ancient world, small differences inevitably began to appear. 'Textual criticism' is the name given to the discipline of comparing different manuscripts, and deciding which of them more faithfully represents the likely original text. In Bible translation the question of textual criticism looms very large.

Until the middle of the twentieth century the earliest surviving manuscripts of the Hebrew Bible dated from the ninth century AD—over a thousand years later than even the latest books of the Hebrew Bible were written. But the discovery of the Dead Sea Scrolls, together with a number of other recent discoveries, have now made available to us manuscripts of the Hebrew text written a thousand years and more earlier. The result has been to confirm the care with which the text had been preserved, even though a number of (mostly minor) differences have emerged.

In addition to Hebrew manuscripts there are full manuscripts of the LXX and other versions from the fourth century AD onwards, and partial texts which are even earlier. These often offer a significantly different reading from the Hebrew text, but this is as likely to be due to the freedom exercised by Greek translators as to a variant Hebrew text to which they had access.

In the case of the New Testament the timescale is less extended. There are complete Greek texts of the New Testament from the fourth century, and many earlier papyri of parts of it have survived, some from as early as the middle of the second century. In all, we have over 5,000 Greek manuscripts of the New Testament, though the majority of these are later and of lesser value. There is again also a wide variety of manuscript evidence for the early versions in Latin, Syriac and Coptic, as well as numerous citations from the New Testament books by early Christian writers whose works are preserved. The New Testament is thus vastly better attested than any other ancient literature. The works of Tacitus, by contrast, survive in only two incomplete manuscripts written many centuries after his time, between them covering only about half of what he is known to have written.

But a large quantity of manuscripts means a large range of variants, since no two manuscripts are exactly alike. Most of the variants are of minor importance, matters of spelling or grammar, or of stylistic variation. Where there are differences of substance, in most cases experts are in little doubt which represents the original. But there remains a significant number of variants where translators must make a choice as to the words to be rendered, or as to whether or not to include a portion of text, which may be as little as one word but may be a whole verse or two. There is room here for sincere disagreement even among those who are well versed in the discipline of textual criticism, and English versions of the Bible may and do differ accordingly.

Many of the most important biblical manuscripts have been discovered relatively recently, and the whole science of textual criticism has become far more sophisticated and, one hopes, more responsible. Translations of the Bible made before the 20th century are thus likely to be based on less reliable texts, as we shall see particularly when we consider what was available to the translators of the Authorized Version. The need for constant retranslation arises not only from the development of the English language, but also from the growing availability of evidence for the original texts themselves.

4
Translation of the Bible into English up to the RSV

Early English Translations

In medieval England Latin was the language of literate people. Direct access to the Bible was restricted in practice to the clergy and monastic orders, and their Bible was the Latin Vulgate. There were a number of translations of parts of the Bible into Old English in the eighth, ninth and tenth centuries. But with the Norman Conquest translations into English virtually ceased, as Norman French became the language of the literate.

We have evidence of a few other translations of sections of the Bible from the fourteenth century. But it was **John Wyclif** (c1330-1384) and his associates who first attempted to put an English Bible in the hands of lay people. The translation is probably mostly not by Wyclif himself, and was revised after his death by his secretary John Purvey, but the project was at the heart of his aim to restore the Bible's authority in the life of church and nation. It was based not on the original languages (which were not available then in

England), but on the Latin Vulgate. Purvey's prologue shows his grasp of the goal of translation, 'to translate after the sentence and not only after the words…; and if the letter may not be followed in the translating, let the sentence ever be whole and open [plain].' Purvey's version was widely read and circulated, despite official condemnation of the Wycliffite movement. It was, in effect, *the* English Bible in the fifteenth and early sixteenth century.

The Sixteenth Century

Two major factors separate later English translations from those of the fourteenth century. The first was the rediscovery in European scholarship of the Hebrew and Greek languages, and the growing availability of biblical texts in the originals. The second was the invention of printing.

The first printed Hebrew Bible appeared in 1488, and the first printed Greek New Testament in 1516. The materials were therefore available for a translation from the originals to be printed in English, and **William Tyndale** (1494-1536) was the first to take up the opportunity. His English New Testament was printed in 1526, not in England, where there was still strong official hostility to a vernacular Bible (particularly one suspected of 'Lutheran' connections), but at Worms, from where it was smuggled into England and met with an enthusiastic black market. Tyndale's translation used a vigorous, idiomatic English style, and his extensively revised 1534 edition was to be the basis of all subsequent English translations until the twentieth century. It was incorporated into the first complete English Bible, printed by Myles Coverdale in 1535—Coverdale's version of the Psalms became the Psalter of the Book of Common Prayer.

Tyndale is by far the most significant figure in the story of the translation of the Bible into English. In addition to his New Testament, he also began the translation of the Hebrew Bible. He published the Pentateuch in English in 1530, and prepared translations of other books which were then incorporated into **'Matthew's Bible'** compiled by Tyndale's associate John Rogers in 1537, and the first English translation to be published 'with the king's most gracious licence.' Bible translation had at last received official approval.

The stage was thus set for an 'authorized version,' which was to be placed in every church in the land, so that 'your parishioners may most commodiously resort to the same and read it.' Coverdale was entrusted with the task of revising the 'Matthew' Bible for this purpose, and the resultant version, issued with a preface by Thomas Cranmer, is known as the **Great Bible** (1539). But it had one significant weakness. Apart from those Hebrew books which Tyndale had translated, the rest of the Old Testament (Coverdale's work) was not based on the Hebrew text. An extensive revision was printed in Geneva in 1560, and was the work of men closely associated with the Reformation movement on the continent. This **'Geneva Bible'** was an immediate success, and was the Bible of the Elizabethan church and of Shakespeare.

King James' Bible

James the First did not share the general enthusiasm for the Geneva Bible, largely on account of the notes published along with the text which were felt to be partisan. So at the Hampton Court Conference summoned in the year after his accession it was agreed to produce a new version, without commentary, 'to be read in the whole Church, and none other.' The work was entrusted to a large group (47 in all) of the best scholars available, who between them represented a range of theological opinion, and so could not be stigmatized as producing a partisan text.

The **King James Bible** of 1611 (popularly known in Britain as the **'Authorized Version'**; this title, even if a little misleading, is so well established that it will be used from here on) claims to be 'newly translated out of the original tongues,' but the translators did not start from scratch. The following clause in the title adds 'with the former translations diligently compared and revised,' and they were in fact instructed to take the Bishops' Bible of 1568 (a revision of the Great Bible) as the basis of their work. The phrases of Tyndale's New Testament can be heard again and again. But their preface ('The Translators to the Reader,' unfortunately not included in most modern editions) makes it clear that they did much more than merely revise the Bishops' Bible (which, after all, was not based directly on the Hebrew text in many Old Testament books), but worked in detail from the original texts.

As conscientious translators, they were well aware of the range of possibilities both in the reading of the original text and in the understanding of its words. So they added marginal notes, not of the 'commentary' type which the king disliked, but to indicate reasonable alternative renderings. In answer to the criticism that such notes undermined the reader's confidence in the text, they replied that 'they that are wise had rather have their judgments at liberty in differences of readings, than to be captivated to one, when it might be the other.'

They chose to avoid 'concordance' translation, whereby the same English word is always used for the same word in the original. They were too good scholars to imagine that words function as mechanically as that, and seem also to have set some store by variety in style, so that at times they vary the English renderings of a given word where the same word would have conveyed the sense perfectly well.

In these and other ways the Authorized Version marked a significant advance on earlier versions, so that even without royal backing it would probably have supplanted even the Geneva Bible in both public and private use. Given the king's strong endorsement as well, it was assured of success. The term 'Authorized Version' is not quite accurate, since (unlike the Book of Common Prayer) it was never imposed by Act of Parliament, but the clause 'appointed to be read in churches' on its title page indicates its quasi-official status. For English Protestants from 1611 to 1881 there was, in effect, only one English Bible.

There is, however, one major weakness which the 1611 version shares with all its predecessors, and which is no fault of its translators. The Hebrew and Greek texts available in the sixteenth and early seventeenth centuries were much inferior to what is available today, and at many points the words rendered by King James' translators are not what is now agreed to be the original text. This problem is particularly serious in the New Testament, for which they were dependent on the Greek text issued by Stephanus in 1550. This text, misleadingly known as the 'Received Text' ('Textus Receptus'), was based on the few Greek manuscripts then available, which were late in date, and represented the 'Byzantine' type of text which most scholars now believe to be a revision (and in some places expansion) of the original. In a few places no Greek text at all was available, and Stephanus' text is taken from the Vulgate, translated back into Greek. The most notorious example is the trinitarian text in 1 John 5.7 ('For there are three that bear record in heaven, the Father, the Word, and the Holy Ghost: and these three are one') which occurs in no Greek manuscript before the fifteenth century where it is clearly derived from the Latin. The discovery of earlier texts and the advances in textual criticism mean that there are now serious textual questions to be set against the undoubted literary qualities of the Authorized Version.

The above discussion may have suggested that Bible translation was an exclusively Protestant enterprise. Certainly Protestants took the lead, but a Catholic response began with the publication of the Rheims New Testament in 1582, followed by the Old Testament published at Douai in 1610. This **'Douai Bible'** was deliberately based not on the Hebrew and Greek but on the Vulgate, the version prescribed by the Council of Trent. Its style was so much based on the Latin as to be quite obscure, and a major revision was undertaken in the eighteenth century. This is what is known as the Douai Bible today.

Translations in the Nineteenth and Early Twentieth Centuries

The Authorized Version had no significant rival for 270 years. There were of course a number of individual efforts at Bible translation, some of them worthy attempts to update the Authorized Version (including one by John Wesley in 1768), others quite eccentric. But none made a lasting impression.

But the Authorized Version, for all its excellence, inevitably became dated in two respects: on the one hand there was the increase of knowledge about the Hebrew and Greek texts noted above, but there was also the fact that no language stands still, and the 'biblical language' of 1611 became increasingly remote from ordinary speech. So a **Revised Version** was produced in 1881 (NT) and 1885 (OT) by a committee set up by the Convocation of Canterbury, drawing on the best biblical scholarship of the time.

It was deliberately a 'revision,' not a new translation. Its compilers aimed to keep as close as possible to the familiar wording, even retaining 'all archaisms, whether of language or construction, which though not in familiar use cause a reader no embarrassment and lead to no misunderstanding.' On one point, however, they clearly felt differently from the 1611 translators, in that they aimed wherever the context allowed to use the same English rendering for the same original word. A parallel (though less conservative) revision process was carried out in America, and the resultant **American Standard Version** of 1901 is thus of recognizably similar character to the Revised Version.

One feature of the new version which was a major contribution to intelligent understanding, was the layout of the printed text. Unlike the Authorized Version, the Revised Version printed the text in sense-paragraphs (though retaining verse-numbers for reference), with some poetical material being set out in lines rather than printed like prose.

The pedantic and archaic style of translation resulting from the revisers' principles, though making it a useful version for close study, was not calculated to excite the reading public and it seems never to have caught the public imagination. But the principle of retranslation was at last recognized, and during the first half of the twentieth century many new versions began to appear. Most of them were the work of individuals, and could claim no official status. Two of these versions may be singled out for special mention.

Two Individual Translations

J Moffatt's vigorous version (New Testament 1913, complete Bible 1928) sometimes reflects Scottish rather than English idiom, but made a decisive break from 'Bible English,' and introduced many for the first time to a Bible in which the characters spoke like real people. Like all individual translations it is at the mercy of the translator's preferences and ideas; does it really help ordinary readers to find at the beginning of the Gospel of John, 'The Logos existed in the very beginning, the Logos was with God, the Logos was divine'? And the introduction of Enoch into the text of 1 Peter 3.19 ('in which also he went' etc) is a rather wild scholarly guess. Moffatt's version remained a solo effort, with no authority but his own.

R A Knox's version (New Testament 1945; complete Bible 1949), on the other hand, received the official endorsement of the Catholic hierarchy, and so stood alongside the Douai Bible as an official version. Like the Douai, it is a translation of the Vulgate, though with careful attention throughout to the original languages. Knox was a master of English style, and his translation is a literary masterpiece. He explained his principles in an important book, *On Englishing the Bible* (1949). Prominent among them is the desire to avoid being merely contemporary. Rather he aimed to produce such good, timeless English that it would not seem dated even in two hundred years' time. Time will tell, but unfortunately for Knox's version it was only another twenty years before a much more widely read Catholic translation, the Jerusalem Bible, appeared.

The Revised Standard Version

But while this wealth of individual Bible translations were being produced, the inadequacy of the more 'official' Revised Version (and its American counterpart) was increasingly felt, and a movement began towards a more extensive revision in the Authorized Version tradition. The result was the **Revised Standard Version** of 1946 (New Testament; whole Bible 1952), a revision by an American committee of the American Standard Version.

The committee's aim was a thorough revision which nonetheless retained the 'qualities which have given to the King James Version a supreme place in English literature.' The Revised and American Standard Versions had retained the archaic verb endings ('-est,' '-eth') and the use of 'thou' instead of the singular 'you;' the new version abandoned these archaisms, except for retaining 'thou' where God is addressed. The American Standard Version's use of 'Jehovah' was dropped again in favour of 'the LORD.' Clearly obsolete forms of expression were replaced, and the language has an altogether more modern feel, though it is far from colloquial.

Poetic material was set out more consistently in lines, and the typography was brought up to date, quotation marks being used for direct speech.

The careful attention to developments in textual criticism which marked the Revised Version was carried further in its successor. One interesting feature is the appearance thirteen times in Isaiah of notes attributing the reading adopted to 'One ancient Ms.' This is the great Isaiah scroll from Qumran, discovered in 1947 and published just in time for the committee to take it into account. This text is more than a thousand years earlier than the ninth century manuscripts edited by the Jewish scribes known as the Masoretes (the 'Masoretic text') on which previous translators had had to depend. It thus marks a significant move forward in translating the Hebrew Bible, comparable with the influence of the great fourth-century codices on the Revised Version of the New Testament.

Updated readings of the Hebrew and Greek texts and (relatively unadventurous) attempts to introduce more modern idiom inevitably attracted conservative criticism and vilification for the new version, including the widespread assertion that its translators were determined to undermine the divinity of Christ. Looking back now it is hard to see what the fuss was about, since the Revised Standard Version is far more conservative and reassuringly familiar in its language than most more recent versions (each of which in its turn has received the same treatment). But the long dominance of the Authorized Version had encouraged a resistance to change which the archaic style of the Revised Version had not seriously threatened, but which now awoke with vigour.

11

5
Modern Translations

From the New English Bible to the Present Day

The Revised Standard Version was still essentially in the tradition of Bible translation going back to Tyndale. It was a revision, not a new translation. There were some more radically new translations in the first half of the twentieth century, but these remained individual contributions. There was still no genuinely new translation by a representative body commanding wide recognition.

The **New English Bible** ('NEB') (1970; as with most translations the NT appeared earlier) was the pioneer. The committee which produced it was set up jointly by many of the Protestant churches in Britain, and contained many of the most respected biblical scholars of the day. They were 'free to employ a contemporary idiom rather than reproduce the traditional "biblical" English,' and were assisted by a panel of 'trusted literary advisers.' The resultant style is certainly 'new,' though many ordinary readers have found it too literary, even 'donnish.' But its publication marked a new era in English Bible translation. Many others soon followed.

The **Jerusalem Bible** ('JB'; 1966) was a new Catholic translation based on the French *Bible de Jérusalem*. It is stylistically elegant, and is widely used by Protestant readers. A **New Jerusalem Bible** ('NJB';1985), following a new edition of the *Bible de Jérusalem* in 1973, is the work of Henry Wansbrough, with an even more elegant and readable style than its predecessor, and making significant steps toward inclusive language. It is distinctive in using 'Yahweh' in place of 'the LORD' to stand for the 'tetragrammaton,' the name of the God of Israel in the OT.

The **New American Bible** ('NAB'; 1970) was produced by members of the Catholic Biblical Association for the Roman Catholic bishops of America. It has a more formal style; the NT, rather hastily prepared, was replaced by a new translation in 1987. The **New American Standard Bible** (1970) was a conservative attempt to update the American Standard Version of 1901. Its English style is sacrificed to literal translation; it is little used outside America.

The **Good News Bible** ('GNB' 1976; also known as **Today's English Version, 'TEV'**) was designed to be suitable for those for whom English is a second language, and so used language which is 'natural, clear, simple and unambiguous.' It follows the principle of 'dynamic equivalence,' resulting in a vigorous and uncluttered style, which has been particularly welcomed among younger people for whom 'Bible English' is an unfamiliar language. It is now in a second edition (1994), with more masculine-oriented features removed and some updating of language.

The **New International Version** ('NIV'; 1978) was translated by a committee representing the evangelical constituency primarily in North America, but with an Anglicized version. It has a moderately contemporary style which reads well in public or in private, and is currently the best-selling version in English. It has been recently published in an inclusive language edition (1996), although other changes are relatively minor.

The **New King James Version** ('NKJV'; 1982) preserves the textual features of the Authorized Version, but with modernized language and spelling. It is a rather quixotic enterprise, inspired by the dominance of the KJV in America, and a backlash against modern textual criticism.

The **New Jewish Version** (or **Tanakh** or New Jewish Publication Society, **NJPS**; 1985) replaced the Jewish Publication Society Bible of 1917. It is a totally new translation, on the 'idiom for idiom' rather than 'word for word' principle.

The **Revised English Bible** ('REB'; 1989) is a radical revision of the NEB, with a much improved style and fairly consistently inclusive language.

The **New Revised Standard Version** ('NRSV'; 1989) is the latest in the line of versions derived from the Authorized. It is a very extensive revision of the RSV, with the last of the 'thous' removed and with the most comprehensive attention to inclusive language yet attempted.

The **New Century Version** ('NCV'; 1991) is a children's or youth version that simplifies the biblical text with a good degree of imagination and rhythmic feeling. There is an anglicized version (1993) and an attractive Youth Bible edition introduced by Steve Chalke.

The **Contemporary English Version** ('CEV'; 1995) is a dynamic equivalence translation that is designed to be heard as well as read clearly and accurately by those who have little English, or for whom English is a second language; hence it has a limited vocabulary. A distinctive feature is that much of the parallelism and repetition in biblical poetry (and in narrative) is minimized—only 3 of the 28 'there is a time for's survive in Ecclesiastes 3.2-8; the result has its own, rather different, rhythm.

The **New Living Translation** ('NLT'; 1996) is a dynamic equivalence translation that is particularly concerned to overcome historical and cultural barriers as well as difficulties of language and sentence structure. It often adds additional words to biblical expressions and metaphors in order to explain them (Song 1.15 'Your eyes are *soft* like doves'—the 'soft' is not in the original but is interpretive and explanatory).

Committees, Individuals and Dialects

Following the lead of the New English Bible most recent committee versions, while drawn up by biblical scholars, have profited from the help of literary consultants. This feature, together with the continuing advances in biblical scholarship and textual criticism, means that Bible translation has entered into a quite new phase since 1960. No previous generation (not even those of Tyndale and of the Authorized Version) has been so well served with versions which both communicate effectively and may be relied on to convey the original sense as nearly as it can be ascertained.

Alongside these committee or 'official' versions, the spate of individual versions has gone on increasing. Even to list them would be impossible. I mention just three which have been or are influential.

J B Phillips, aware that young people no longer understood 'Bible English,' produced his famous *Letters to Young Churches* in 1947 and completed the New Testament in 1958 and *Four Prophets* in 1963. His style is lively paraphrase, sometimes colloquial to the point of inelegance, but vigorous and arresting. In the days before the Good News Bible, Phillips filled a significant gap particularly for younger readers, and is still widely read today.

A more idiosyncratic paraphrase is the **Living Bible** of Kenneth Taylor (1971), in very colloquial American idiom, and giving clear expression to the author's conservative theology. ('The theological lodestar in this book has been a rigid evangelical position.') But as a result of aggressive marketing it has probably been more widely read than any other individual version in recent years. The New Living Version is being marketed as its successor, but is in fact a new translation.

The Message (NT: 1993; OT wisdom books and Psalms 1996) is a vivid rewriting by Eugene Peterson—not so much a paraphrase as an interpretation using contemporary metaphors, idioms and wordplays. Its impact on many Christians may be compared to that of The Living Bible for an earlier generation. Only some of the OT has been translated as yet and it is not anglicized. There are no verse numbers.

All these versions are, or intend to be, in 'standard English' (though most of the primarily American versions have 'anglicized editions' available separately). But attempts have also been made to translate the Bible or parts of it into non-standard English. Thus I possess *The Gospels in Scouse*, and *Chapters from the New Testament translated into the Wensleydale Tongue*, and no doubt there are many more. Some such versions are no doubt done for fun rather than as a serious attempt to communicate in non-standard English, but a much more serious version is W L Lorimer, *The New Testament in Scots* (Penguin, 1983), based on a lifetime of study of the Scots language. Here is Matthew 5.14-15: 'Ye are the licht o the warld. A toun biggit on a hill-tap canna be hoddit; an again, whan fowk licht a lamp, they pit-it-na ablò a meal-bassie, but set it up on the dresserheid, and syne it gíes licht for aabodie i the houss.'

6
Some Issues in Bible Translation

The Text To Be Translated

We have noted that some English versions were made from the Latin (notably Wyclif, Coverdale, Douai, Knox), and these days many translations made into African, Asian and Latin American languages are made from an English version by translators who do not know Hebrew and Greek. Such 'secondary translation' is regrettable, and fortunately now no English translation which was not based on the Hebrew and Greek would be taken seriously. But which Hebrew and Greek texts should be used?.

The dramatic increase in known manuscripts and advances in text-critical method mean that we are not now in the position of the King James translators to whom only a comparatively faulty text was available. The translator who is not an expert in textual criticism may with a great deal of confidence work from the currently published critical texts. But where manuscript evidence is divided critics are sometimes not in agreement, and a translator must take sides over the omission or inclusion of a suspect verse, or over which of two words is more likely to have been in the original text. At such times at least a basic acquaintance with the highly specialized science of textual criticism is needed.

However, in contrast with earlier attempts, modern translation at least starts from an agreed text. For the New Testament, the agreed starting point is the Greek text published by the United Bible Societies, also available from the German Bible Society (the 'Nestle-Aland' edition), the only difference being in their 'critical apparatus'—the information given about variation between different manuscripts that were considered in agreeing the final form of the text.[1] For the Hebrew Bible, the agreed starting point is known as Biblia Hebraica Stuttgartensia—or BHS for short.

'Literal' versus 'Dynamic' Translation[2]

Any translator is faced with the competing demands of the desire, on the one hand, to be as faithful as possible to the original and, on the other, to produce a version which communicates well and is a pleasure to read. The more widely differing the structures of the languages involved, the greater

---

1   At each disputed reading, the UBS edition gives the text printed a rating from A (virtually certain) to D (a high degree of doubt). A companion volume, Bruce Metzger's *A Textual Commentary on the Greek New Testament* explains in lay terms the reasons for each decision.
2   The word 'literal' is used with slightly different meanings in different contexts. Most often, it has the sense 'not figurative or metaphorical' when applied to the meaning or interpretation of a text. Here, I am using it in the sense of translating 'word-for-word' in contrast to the approach of translating 'idiom-for-idiom.'

this tension becomes.

But for the Bible translator there is the additional feature that the very words of the text to be translated are regarded by some of the potential readers, and perhaps by the translators themselves, as the product of divine inspiration. The form, as well as the content, of the original may thus come to be regarded as sacrosanct, and the only acceptable version is one which mirrors as closely as possible the grammatical structures and vocabulary of the Hebrew or Greek text. Such an attitude resembles the Muslim insistence that there can never be a 'translation' of the Quran, only interpretations, since it is the Arabic text itself which is the locus of divine inspiration.

As we have seen, this view can result in translations which are so literal as to be at best stilted, if not virtually unintelligible (such as Aquila's Greek Old Testament, the first Wyclif translation before revision by John Purvey, and to a lesser degree the New American Standard Bible). Such unidiomatic versions are defended as faithfully reproducing the sacred text. Anything else is 'paraphrase,' which has often been used as a term of disapprobation: 'paraphrase' allows the translator's own ideas to intrude into the text, so that the authority of the original is relativized.

Over against this literalistic tendency stands the philosophy of translation which has come to be known as 'dynamic equivalence,' a term which has come to prominence particularly in the context of the continuing enterprise of translating the Bible into the thousands of languages which so far have no Bible version. On this view it is not the form of the text which matters, but its content, and it is the translator's responsibility to render that sense into the target language in whatever way will best communicate to native speakers of that language, without regard to such matters as the grammatical structure, word-order, vocabulary, or cultural features of the original. Translations produced this way are typically more free, readable and elegant, and can fit more comfortably into the cultural context of the intended readers, but are often suspected of having adulterated the sacred text.

The Good News Bible, produced for the Bible Societies, was a self-conscious paradigm of 'dynamic equivalence.' But in fact virtually all English versions of the last half-century have accepted the principle of translating idiom for idiom rather than word for word, even though the degree of freedom exercised has varied. Thus even the relatively conservative New International Version, regarded by some as veering towards literalism, while it lists as its first concern 'the accuracy of the translation and its fidelity to the thought of the biblical writers' (notice 'thought,' not 'words'), also affirms that 'faithful communication of the meaning of the writers of the Bible demands frequent modifications in sentence structure and constant regard for the contextual meanings of words.' The resultant translation claims, with considerable justification, to be in 'clear and natural English.'

The Problem of Religious Conservatism

Conservatism, in the sense of resistance to change, seems to affect people in matters of religion more readily than in other areas. Thoroughly modern, liberated people with radical political views may still be found as staunch advocates of the Authorized Version and the Book of Common Prayer. Saint Luke long ago summed up the typical reaction to change in matters of religion: 'The old is good' (Luke 5.39). This is a hurdle which every Bible translator must face.

I attended an English-speaking service in a remote hill-station in Nigeria shortly after *Good News for Modern Man* was published. After reading a passage from the new version (which had been designed for precisely that sort of situation where English was at best a second language) the Nigerian leader of the service put it down saying, 'Now we will hear it from the real Bible,' and proceeded to read the same passage from the Authorized Version. The same devotion to the Authorized Version as the 'real Bible' is still to be found in many English congregations, after decades of 'better' translations being freely available. To talk of a corrupt text and of language which does not communicate to most people today cuts no ice: the Bible is expected to speak in Elizabethan English, and anything more 'modern' is inferior and dangerous. The colloquial language which Tyndale employed so that the Scriptures would be accessible to the ploughboy has become the sacred language of religion, and the more remote it is from ordinary speech the more special and holy it seems.

The task of Bible translation is much easier where there is no existing version to be supplanted. I met a translator who had been commissioned to produce a dynamic new translation for a tribe in Zaire who already had a Bible version, translated from the Authorized Version and so literalistic as to be quite remote from the current form of the language. He told me how he read out his fresh, new, colloquial version with pride, and people commented favourably on how easy it was to understand, but then pointed that of course it wasn't the Bible. It almost seems that by definition the Bible must be remote and unintelligible. The Hebrew prophets with their vigorous contemporary idioms and the New Testament writers with their 'market Greek' would be horrified!

Public and Private Reading

In our day when reading books is overwhelmingly a private activity it is as well to be reminded that the biblical books were written in a period of widespread illiteracy, and many of them were probably originally designed for public reading. And even today, while most books are translated for private reading, Bible translators have to reckon with the fact that their work is likely to be read out in church, as part of an act of worship—and, as with the Dramatized Bible, may even work with this concern to the fore.

One implication of this is that a translator must beware of expressions which, while perfectly clear in print, may be ambiguous or worse when heard orally. There is no visible punctuation to guide the hearer, and one cannot rely on the skill of every church reader being sufficient to avoid misconstructions of sentences where punctuation is the only way of differentiating two meanings. For example, Romans 8.33-34 can sound very different from what Paul intended if read aloud as: 'Who will bring any charge against God's elect? It is God/who justifies. Who is to condemn? It is Christ Jesus/ who died...' Some translation committees have therefore wisely made a point of having their proposed translations read aloud before agreeing them.

The make-up of a typical congregation makes heavy demands on a translator's skill. There will be some who love the reassuring old words of the Authorized Version, and others whose concern is to hear something which communicates directly in lively, contemporary style. Some will set great store by the dignity of the language, others by its freshness and ability to challenge. To satisfy all tastes is an impossible task, and the translator who has an eye to public reading will usually settle for a compromise.

But the wide range of types of translation available, while it may be confusing for the newcomer, allows those responsible for public worship the chance to select a version suitable for each particular group and occasion.

Some versions, however, are not designed for public reading. More literal versions which do not read like good English may nonetheless be helpful for close, analytical study of the text by those who are not able to work in the original languages. Colloquial paraphrases like the Living Bible, which would generally be quite unsuitable for public reading, may arrest the attention of a new Bible reader or stimulate others to new ways of looking at the text.

Inclusive Language

In the latter part of the twentieth century the traditional English use of 'men' to mean 'people,' 'he' as a pronoun for an unspecified person of either sex, and so on, has become increasingly unacceptable, and Bible versions have been adapted accordingly. Thus while the Revised Standard Version, the Jerusalem Bible, the New English Bible, and the New International Version happily continued to use the 'generic masculine,' their revisions in the 1980s and 1990s have gone to great lengths to be inclusive wherever the original did not appear to be gender-specific.

Such accommodation to modern sensibilities is easily lampooned as 'trendy' and 'politically correct,' but it is in fact simply good translation. Thus the Greek *anthropos* (human being), while it is masculine in form, is usually clearly differentiated from *aner* (a male person), and to use the same English term 'man' for both was always liable to distort the sense. It has taken modern sensitivity to exclusive language to alert us to the poverty of the English language in this respect, and to send us in search of better ways of conveying the sense of the original.

But of course Hebrew and Greek also use generic masculine pronouns and terms of address such as 'brothers' when clearly the whole church community is in view. In the current climate of thought many female readers feel excluded by such terms. Once that is the case, to continue to offer literal renderings is actually to misrepresent the biblical writers, by obscuring the inclusiveness of their intention, though there is room for dispute in many cases over whether the original did intend to be inclusive, and as to how far a translator may responsibly obscure the patriarchal culture which underlies many of the masculines of the Bible.

Inclusive translation is an art in itself. There are certain well-tried devices, such as turning singular generic statements into the plural (and thus substituting 'they' for 'he'), or using the first or second person in place of the third where the context allows the sense to be conveyed in this way. Words like 'people,' 'humanity,' or 'mortals' can be used in place of 'man,' 'men,' or 'mankind.' But there is the danger that by reducing the range of vocabulary available the translation may be made less elegant, for example by too many uses of 'people' in a short space. And there are disputes as to how far English idiom is yet ready to accept terms like 'humans,' 'humankind,' or whether it allows a 'whoever' to be followed by a 'they.' Usage is fluid, and judgments as to what is currently acceptable will vary. But the issue will not go away, and it is hard to imagine any new translation from now on perpetuating the generic masculines of the traditional versions.

There are further problems for the Bible translator in this area. 'Fishers of men' is a well-loved phrase, and aptly echoes the preceding mention of 'fishermen.' It is hard to see how an inclusive version can retain the familiar phrase, or match the elegance of the word-play. Or what of Jesus' regular self-designation as 'the Son of Man,' a phrase which literally means a human being? If 'the son of man' in Psalm 8.4 becomes 'human beings,' what are we to do with Hebrews 2.6 where on the basis of that verse the writer sees the psalm as pointing to Jesus? Even with generous use of footnotes, such issues are not easily resolved, and the Bible translator does not have the luxury of writing a commentary on his or her text!

All this is to do with biblical ways of speaking about people. Feminist discomfort with masculine language about God (a masculine devil seems to have been found less offensive!) has not yet been reflected in Bible translation. This has rightly been regarded by translators as a different issue from the exclusion of half the human race by pronouns.

7

Choosing an English Version

Philip Jenson

With the multiplication of versions, it is becoming difficult to choose a Bible to work with, whether as an individual or for use in groups or in church services. There are many criteria that are relevant to this decision: accuracy, freedom in changing the syntax and imagery of the original, range of vocabulary, explanation of unusual idioms or customs, readability, inclusive language policy, rhythm, layout (subheadings, length of line, the extent to which poetry is indicated, style of verse numbering), study aids (footnotes, cross-references, apocrypha), and cost. A translation or paraphrase has had to choose which of these features it will emphasize, and consequently which ones it will make secondary. The reason for this choice is usually related to the readership in mind and to the way in which these readers will use the version. Of course, most will want to use a Bible for several different purposes, and no one version will be the ideal for every occasion.

Required uses that could influence the choice of version include:

(i) in-depth Bible study (where one would look for accuracy, a literal translation, an apocrypha—there is none available for NIV, CEV, NLT, NCV);

(ii) reading long sections, or reading out aloud (readability, simplicity);

(iii) explaining the Christian faith to outsiders (simplicity, clear explanation of theological terms and cultural features, inclusive language);

(iv) memorizing the Bible (accuracy, rhythm);

(v) communicating to those with a basic education, or for whom English is a second language (simplicity, narrow range of vocabulary).

Cost is hopefully secondary, but new translations usually come first in more expensive hardback editions; cheaper ones and study versions follow later.

Of the many versions mentioned in the last section, six stand out: NRSV, NIV, REB, NLT, GNB, CEV. They range from the more literal end of the spectrum (NRSV) through to making extensive use of dynamic equivalence (CEV). Each of them has strong points and weaknesses. Take, for example Ps 1.1–2:

NRSV 1 Happy are those
who do not follow the advice of the wicked,
or take the path that sinners tread,
or sit in the seat of scoffers;
2 but their delight is in the law of the LORD,
and on his law they meditate day and night.

NIV 1 Blessed are those
who do not walk in the counsel of the wicked

or stand in the way of sinners
  or sit in the seat of mockers.
2 But their delight is in the law of the Lord,
  and on his law they meditate day and night.

REB   1 Happy is the one
  who does not take the counsel of the wicked for a guide,
  or follow the path that sinners tread,
  or take his seat in the company of scoffers.
2 His delight is in the law of the Lord;
  it is his meditation day and night.

NLT   1 Oh, the joys of those
  who do not follow the advice of the wicked,
  or stand around with sinners,
  or join in with scoffers.
2 But they delight in doing everything the Lord wants;
  day and night they think about his law.

GNB[2] 1 Happy are those who reject the advice of evil people,
  who do not follow the example of sinners
  or join those who have no use for God.
2 Instead, they find joy in obeying the Law of the Lord,
  and they study it day and night.

CEV   1 God blesses those people who refuse evil advice
  and won't follow sinners
  or join in sneering at God.
2 Instead, the Law of the Lord makes them happy,
  and they think about it day and night.

There are difficult choices to be made between the accuracy of a more literal translation, and the simplicity or acceptability of a paraphrase, for something is always lost as well as gained in paraphrase. The CEV's simplicity is illustrated by its decision that its readers will not understand the form 'happy are those who ...' and to turn it into a simple statement ('God blesses'). But in so doing it subtly changes the mood and function of the original. Along with the GNB it has chosen simpler words for 'meditate' and 'scoffers.' However, they both retain 'law' (for Torah), a concept that is often misunderstood by Christians. The NLT paraphrases in such a way that its close link with the Lord's will is clearer.

Since the recent publication of the new edition of the NIV, five of the six versions now use gender-inclusive language, and they achieve this by putting the singulars into the plural ('Blessed are those ...'). The REB begins inclusive but individualizes with the masculine pronoun in the next verse ('his delight'). Making singulars into plurals is a good way to inclusivize a text, but it loses the particular and individual character of the original Hebrew. The REB's 'the one' is a good attempt, but even this is somewhat formal and cannot be sustained in verse 2.

The metaphor of a three-stage progressive journey in the first verse (walk, stand, sit) is captured only by the NIV, which in this case (but not elsewhere) has retained the traditional translation. However, only the NLT accurately conveys the structure of the verse by its layout. By explaining the text, paraphrases may also decide on one interpretation in a verse that is open to more than one. Thus GNB and CEV specify that the wicked scoff at God, but the original allows the scoffing to include other members of the community as well. Poetry by its very nature is open, complex and full of condensed images, all of which make reading demanding. Yet it is these inevitable 'difficulties' that paraphrases are dedicated to overcoming. It is generally true that paraphrases are least successful in capturing the elusive and evocative character of poetry—although an impatient reader might well give up on a traditional translation before understanding it!

Let us look at a passage from an NT epistle with some complex argument (Romans 3.24-25):

NRSV   24 they are now justified by his grace as a gift, through the redemption that is in Christ Jesus, 25 whom God put forward as a sacrifice of atonement by his blood, effective through faith.

NIV   24 and are justified freely by his grace through the redemption that came by Christ Jesus. 25 God presented him as a sacrifice of atonement, through faith in his blood.

REB   24 and all are justified by God's free grace alone, through his act of liberation in the person of Christ Jesus. 25 For God designed him to be the means of expiating sin by his death, effective through faith.

NLT   24 Yet now God in his gracious kindness declares us not guilty. He has done this through Christ Jesus, who has freed us by taking away our sins. 25 For God sent Jesus to take the punishment for our sins and to satisfy God's anger against us. We are made right with God when we believe that Jesus shed his blood, sacrificing his life for us.

GNB[2] 24 But by the free gift of God's grace all are put right with him through Christ Jesus, who sets them free. 25 God offered him, so that by his blood [GNB[1] has 'sacrificial death'] he should become the means by which people's sins are forgiven through their faith in him.

CEV   24 But God treats us much better than we deserve, and because of Christ Jesus, he freely accepts us and sets us free from our sins. 25 God sent Christ to be our sacrifice. Christ offered his life's blood, so that by faith in him we could come to God.

The NLT explains in most detail; compare the free approach of *The Message*:

Message Out of sheer generosity he put us in right standing with himself. A pure gift. He got us out of the mess we're in and restored us to where he always wanted us to be. And he did it by means of Jesus Christ. God sacrificed Jesus on the altar of the world to clear the world of sin. Having faith in him sets us in the clear.

The paraphrases are united in finding substitutes for the theological term 'justify,' but this is not just a theological term, it is also a legal and covenantal term. Only the NLT retains the crucial forensic (legal) context of Paul's argument. CEV has (probably rightly) decided that 'grace' is also generally misunderstood, and so substitutes a phrase. NLT and GNB retain the root, but add further clarifying words. The more literal translations assume readers know the meaning of these words, or perhaps they encourage them to find out. The 'sacrifice of atonement' translates a difficult Greek word whose meaning here depends on a theological as much as a lexical judgment. The problem solved by Christ's death may be sin (REB, GNB, CEV) or God's anger (NLT) or it may be left open (NRSV, NIV). Both for this word and for 'redemption,' the OT background is essential background for understanding Paul's argument. It is likely that the meaning of 'sacrifice' as used in the Bible is as easily misunderstood today as is 'law.' In dense epistles like Romans, translation for those who know little about the rest of the Bible is even more difficult than usual. What is needed may be an interpretation rather than a paraphrase, or even a planned reading strategy, so that readers are helped to appreciate the cultural and theological context in which Paul is writing (for instance, the significance of sacrifice and blood).

These examples may be multiplied, but even from these two examples it is possible to see how the versions range from the more literal (NRSV, NIV) to the more free and interpretive (GNB, CEV). The vocabulary of some translations also tends to be wider and more learned (REB, NRSV) while paraphrases often restrict themselves to a narrower range (with CEV the most restricted). The latest editions of the NIV (inclusivised) and GNB (lightly revised) are in general more dated, both in language and scholarship.

Translation or Paraphrase?

Should we prefer a more literal translation or a freer paraphrase? In the Bible, the repetition of words, the syntax of sentences, and the imagery is of greater importance than we sometimes imagine. Paraphrases often make drastic changes, sometimes clarifying but also sometimes distorting the original. But changes to the original are inevitable even in the most literal translation. Further, the most accurate translation is no use if it cannot be understood by the reader. A paraphrase that communicates only a fraction of the original is better than nothing (and, of course, is always sufficient for salvation). We are often unaware how many demands a literal translation makes on a reader unfamiliar with biblical language and culture.

But emphasizing the difficulty of translation is only one side. Through the gracious work of the Spirit, good translations and paraphrases can also enhance and adorn the original. Like a good sermon they can illuminate the significance of the scriptures for today by stimulating the mind and exciting the imagination in ways that may go beyond the original text, but are not

23

repugnant to it. A good case can be made for using two versions: a more literal translation for study and memorization; and a paraphrase for reading long sections of the Bible, for communicating with learners and outsiders, and for discovering new perspectives on texts that are in danger of becoming too familiar.

Bibliography

The introduction to a translation often sets out the history, rationale and translation policy of the version. For further insight, there is often a book about the version written by one of its chief translators. The issues are probably best appreciated by reading the same text in several versions. Look at your favourite passages and texts from different biblical genres. A selection might include narrative (Genesis 1.1–2.3—the creation; John 1.1–18—the word made flesh), law (Exodus 20.1–17—the ten commandments), speech (Deuteronomy 6.1–9—'Hear, O Israel'; Matthew 5.1–16—the Beatitudes), poetry (Psalm 23—'The Lord is my shepherd'), wisdom literature (Proverbs 16; Ecclesiastes 3.1–8—'There is a time for'), prophecy (Isaiah 40—'comfort my people;' Hosea 11—'When Israel was a child'), epistle (Romans 8.31–39— 'Who will separate us'; 1 Corinthians 13—love; Philippians 2.1–11—'he emptied himself') and apocalyptic (Revelation 20—the millennium). The following books are also helpful:

Anchor Bible Dictionary, Volume VI, pp 787-851. Various authors. A good survey of both ancient and modern versions.

Bruce, F F , *History of the Bible in English* (3rd ed; Oxford: OUP, 1978)—a good historical survey of the translations and their policies up to 1978.

Duthie, A S, *How to Choose Your Bible Wisely* (Carlisle: Paternoster Press, 1994)—compares the various versions with the help of many tables but curiously comes down in favour of the GNB.

Greenslade, S L, (ed) *The Cambridge History of the Bible Vol. 3. The West from the Reformation to the Present Day* (Cambridge: CUP, 1970)—a standard survey of the period.

Hargreaves, C, *A Translator's Freedom: Modern English Bibles and their Language* (Sheffield: JSOT, 1993)—a good study of the issues raised by translation and paraphrase.

Lewis, J P, *The English Bible: from KJV to NIV: A History and Evaluation* (2nd ed; Grand Rapids: Baker, 1991)—a detailed analysis and positive assessment of the various versions up to and including the NRSV.

Nida, E A and Taber C R, *The Theory and Practice of Translation* (Leiden: 1969)—Nida is the key theoretical thinker behind the principle of 'dynamic equivalence.'

Perry, M, *The Dramatised Bible* (London: Marshall Pickering/Bible Society, 1990)— assigns biblical passages to several voices for performance in church or groups; however, it is often almost as easy to do this with the version of your choice by simply assigning narrator and speaking characters.

UAE
BUSINESS
GUIDE

there's more to life...
ask**explorer**.com

UAE Business Guide 2014/1st Edition
1st Edition 2014   ISBN 978-9948-22-285-9

Explorer Publishing & Distribution
PO Box 34275, Dubai
United Arab Emirates
Phone   +971 (0)4 340 8805
Fax   +971 (0)4 340 8806
Email   info@askexplorer.com
Web   askexplorer.com

WELCOME...

…to the *UAE Business Guide*, your comprehensive resource for setting up a business in the UAE. Packed with information, yet broken down into manageable sections, this guide will help you every step of the way to setting up your own business.

With 20 years' experience of helping UAE expats cut through the red tape, Explorer knows how daunting all the processes and procedures can be, and perhaps none more confusing than those required to set up a business. But Explorer also knows, first hand, what a fantastic place the UAE is to develop a successful business, and so we bring you the *UAE Business Guide*.

You bring the passion, innovation and ambition, and we'll provide the rest.

There's more to life...
The Explorer Team

The UAE is a thriving, cosmopolitan marketplace, but one that is constantly growing and changing. We know that procedures and fees can change so, for the latest news and updates, make askexplorer.com your online companion. Alternatively, if you have any comments relating to the information in this book, we'd love to hear from you. Have you found this book helpful? Do you have any advice for our readers? Email us at info@askexplorer.com.

RAK FREE TRADE ZONE
THE GATEWAY TO FAST-GROWING GLOBAL MARKETS

Ras Al Khaimah (RAK) is one of the seven emirates which comprise the United Arab Emirates (UAE), along with Abu Dhabi and Dubai. RAK has earned a reputation as a business-friendly, world-class investment environment. The cost of living and doing business in RAK is 25 to 50 per cent lower than the UAE average, allowing companies to maximise their return on investment.

RAK has three free zones, including the Ras Al Khaimah Free Trade Zone (RAK FTZ), the investment destination of choice for more than 7,500 companies from over 100 countries, representing more than 50 industry sectors.

Why invest in Ras Al Khaimah?

- ▸ 100% Foreign Ownership
- ▸ No Taxation
- ▸ Less than an Hour Drive from Dubai
- ▸ Quick and Easy Company Set-Up

- ▸ Complete, Cost-Effective Packages Including Licenses and Facilities starting from USD 4,000
- ▸ Eligibility for UAE Residence Visas

 ## Flexi Facilities

- ▶ Commercial or Consultancy Licences
- ▶ Furnished, Semi-Enclosed Work Stations
- ▶ Option to Upgrade to an Executive Office or Warehouse

 ## Offices

- ▶ Commercial, Consultancy or General Trading Licences
- ▶ Private Furnished/Customisable Office Space
- ▶ Full Accessibility 24/7

 ## Warehouses

- ▶ Commercial, General Trading or Industrial Licences
- ▶ Warehouses in Various Sizes Starting from 205 m²
- ▶ On-Site Labour and Staff Accommodation Availability

 ## Industrial Land

- ▶ Commercial, General Trading or Industrial Licences
- ▶ Leases and Ready-to-Build Plots Starting from 2,500 m²
- ▶ On-Site Staff Accommodation

Find out what 7,500 companies have already discovered.

Contact one of our business development professionals for more information.

UAE (Ras Al Khaimah) Tel: +971 7 2041111, (Dubai) Tel: +971 4 7041875, (Abu Dhabi) Tel: +971 2 6994888
Germany (Cologne) Tel: +49 221 5708650 - Turkey (Istanbul) Tel: +90 216 6884875 - India (Mumbai) Tel: +91 22 22042223

RAK Free Trade Zone Authority - Government of Ras Al Khaimah
Tel: +971 7 2041111 - Email: info@rakftz.com - Website: www.rakftz.com

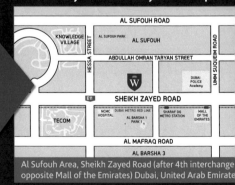

CONTENTS

INTRODUCTION

This is your guide to setting up, running and managing your small or medium-sized business in the UAE. You've got a great idea, but how do you bring it to life? Within these pages, we are giving you the tools to go out and turn your great idea into a successful enterprise.

While the UAE is a wonderfully buoyant, optimistic place to set up a company as an expat, there's plenty of red tape that can turn a brainwave into a headache before you've even printed your business cards. Between government ministries, bank loans, free zones authorities, PROs, sponsorship laws, not to mention the cultural sensitivities… where do you even start?

Whatever industry you want to position yourself in, whatever your audience, and even if you already have an existing business, we've got plenty of advice and information to help you, from the planning stages to getting off the ground, and beyond.

The guide is divided into chapters that take you through all the setup stages, generally in the order that you'll come to them:

Working In The UAE
Need some convincing about whether the UAE is the right place to set up? This chapter details the pros and cons of living and working in the 'sandpit', from the cost of living to cultural dos and don'ts, and the lifestyle you can expect from this perennially sunny, tax-free environment.

Setting Up A Business
This chapter is packed with the nitty gritty information, and breaks down all the options. Choose the trade licence that will best suit the activities of your business. Find out about the issues and costs surrounding free zones and mainland businesses. We've detailed the legal considerations, including everything you need to think about when it comes to employing staff. You'll also find plenty of advice from professionals in the industry, as well as from fellow entrepreneurs.

Doing Business
Whether you're travelling to the UAE to meet with associates or scouting potential opportunities, we've got some tips on the local cultural, social and business etiquette. And, now that it's time to really get down to business, we've got some great ideas for inspiring workspaces as well as advice on networking and finding support. You'll also find some suggestions on unique spaces to hold events, and venues to host the perfect working lunch.

Women In Business

Whoever said that business is a man's world was wrong, and we've got the proof. This chapter is packed with inspirational case studies on some of the UAE's leading businesswomen, including the 'Mompreneurs' who are striving to have it all. We've also detailed some business networks aimed specifically at women.

PLUS...

How Tos

You'll find these step-by-step guides to what can be mind-boggling procedures throughout the book. Cut through the red tape and find out where to go, what to take with you and how to complete the minefield of steps required to get a trade licence, lease a commercial premises, and more.

If you're looking for a specific procedure, check the list of How Tos:

Case Studies

We've dotted the book with inspirational and informative real-life stories from business owners in the UAE. These are the people that have done it and succeeded, and they offer some valuable advice.

So, what are you waiting for? Good luck!

Directory

Here you'll find the important contacts and resources you'll need to get things done, especially the government departments.

WHSmith

Oasis Mall • Dubai Mall • Wafi Mall
Al Wahda Mall Abu Dhabi • Yas Mall
Marina Mall • Jw Marriott • Executive Towers
Sharjah University Hospital • Abu Dhabi Airport

Newspapers & Magazines
Books & Stationery
Drinks & Snacks

WORKING IN THE UAE

UAE
IN A NUTSHELL

THE MSCI EMERGING MARKETS INDEX ALTERED THE STATUS OF THE UAE FROM 'FRONTIER MARKET' TO 'EMERGING MARKET' IN MID-2014 ON THE BASIS OF ITS STOCKS PERFORMANCE

DUBAI'S STOCK MARKET MADE A

200%

GAIN SINCE THE BEGINNING OF 2013

THE UAE POPULATION HAS GROWN RAPIDLY IN RECENT YEARS TO 9 MILLION

The United Arab Emirates is quite possibly one of the most cosmopolitan countries in the world. Located in the heart of the Middle East, it is home to more than 200 nationalities and is one of the most progressive, open-minded countries in the region.

World Central

Historically, the UAE has been a strategic trading hub between east and west, with Dubai earning a reputation as the 'city of merchants'. Sharjah was home to the first international airport in the region, forming an important stop-gap between the UK and India during the British Raj. With huge oil reserves in the emirate of Abu Dhabi and globally important container ports on both the west coast and in the eastern coastal cities of Fujairah and Khor Fakkan, the economy of the UAE has been thriving since its foundation in 1971.

The resulting development was rapid and, despite a blip in 2009 when the bubble burst in the wake of the global economic crisis, the UAE has become a socio-economic beacon in an otherwise unstable region. The country's economy is well and truly back on track and the UAE continues to be a land of opportunity.

Land Of Opportunity

Low-cost labourers from the Indian Subcontinent arrive in huge volumes to keep profit margins in the construction industry high. A thriving service industry – a massive contributing factor in the tourism and hospitality sector – employs hundreds of thousands of South Asian expats in hotels, restaurants, spas and so on. Western-educated expats relocate in droves to sample a taste of the tax-free, perennially sunny good life that such a booming service industry affords. And tourists from around the world arrive in their millions each year to enjoy this unique destination.

Emirati nationals themselves, while taking up a relatively low proportion of the country's population, enjoy an extremely good standard of living. Government policies award nationals with houses and financial benefits, the presence of globally renowned educational institutions produce highly-educated, bilingual Emirati graduates, and Emiratisation programmes keep them in well-paid jobs. Not to mention the reliance on Emirati sponsors for foreign business; locals in general have money to burn that trickles through every industry imaginable.

It's all good news for entrepreneurs who can take advantage of this dynamic economy: high disposable incomes, low cost labour... a slice of the pie is yours for the taking.

THE UAE HAS BECOME A SOCIO-ECONOMIC BEACON IN AN OTHERWISE UNSTABLE REGION

THE UAE

The vast majority of the UAE's growth has come from foreign workers moving to the country, and the local population now accounts for less than 20%. However, aside from the huge number of Indians settling in the UAE, Emirati nationals still make up the largest ethnic group and have considerable influence.

Weather

The UAE only really experiences two seasons: hot and hotter. Without a doubt the best time to live and enjoy the country is from October to April, when it's mostly blue skies and temperatures of 10°C (50°F) to 24°C (75°F). Every day in the winter is a sunny reminder of why you chose to live here – tepid sea water to swim in, cloudless skies to sunbathe under, and warm, comfortable evenings for alfresco dining.

However, during the summer months (between May and September), be prepared for scorching temperatures that can exceed a sweltering 48°C (118°), and high humidity levels. Yes, it's undeniably hot, but the UAE is well and truly geared up for it with AC in every mall, restaurant, office and even many bus shelters, to keep sweaty brows at bay.

Area

The total land area of the UAE is approximately 83,600 sq km, with around 1,318km of coastline. Abu Dhabi accounts for a

Burj Al Arab

huge 67,340 sq km of that total. While not particularly mountainous, the highest named point is Jebel Yibir at 1,572m, 'jebel' meaning mountain or hill in Arabic. The UAE's coordinates are 24°00'North 54°00'East.

Flag

The UAE flag incorporates the Pan-Arab colours of green, white, black and red, symbolising Arabian unity. It was adopted on 2 December 1971 as the official flag of the country. Interestingly, each of the seven emirates, aside from Fujairah, also has its own flag, all of which use just red and white.

Population

The UAE population has grown rapidly in recent years as expat arrivals, robust economic expansion and high birth rates have continued to push up the total number. According to the World Bank, the UAE's population was just 322,439, a year after the country was formed, in 1972.

By 2002, 30 years later, that figure had ballooned by 10 times to just over 3.2 million. After 40 years, population has now grown by over 28 times the 1972 figure, currently recorded at around 9.2 million.

Currency

The monetary unit is the dirham (Dhs. or AED – Arab Emirate Dirham), which is divided into 100 fils. On notes, all denominations are marked in both Arabic and English, although coin values are shown only in Arabic. Notes come in denominations of Dhs.5 (brown), Dhs.10 (green), Dhs.20 (light blue), Dhs.50 (purple), Dhs.100 (pink), Dhs.200 (yellowy-brown), Dhs.500 (blue) and Dhs.1,000 (browny-purple).

All coins are silver in colour, with a total of six in circulation, but you typically only come across the three largest denominations: Dhs.1, 50 fils and 25 fils. The dirham has been pegged to the US dollar since 1980, at a mid-rate of $1 to Dhs.3.6725.

Time Zone

The UAE is four hours ahead of UTC (Universal Coordinated Time, formerly known as GMT). Clocks are not altered for daylight saving in the summer, so when Europe and North America gain an hour in spring, the time difference becomes slightly shorter. Time differences between the UAE and some cities around the world (not allowing for any daylight savings in those cities) are: Bangkok +3, Hong Kong +4; London -4; Los Angeles -12; Moscow -1; New York -9; Sydney +6; and Tokyo +5.

EVERY DAY IN THE WINTER IS A SUNNY REMINDER OF WHY YOU CHOSE TO LIVE HERE – TEPID SEA WATER TO SWIM IN, CLOUDLESS SKIES TO SUNBATHE UNDER, AND WARM, COMFORTABLE EVENINGS FOR ALFRESCO DINING

ECONOMY

According to most financial experts, the outlook for the economy of the United Arab Emirates is remarkably bright. Less than five years ago the global economic crisis was taking a fair swipe at the country, with Dubai in particular becoming something of a poster child for the boom or bust era, so it's been a particularly impressive turnaround.

The International Monetary Fund (IMF) changed its initial prediction of growth for the UAE's economy in 2014 from a forecast of 3.9% made in October 2013, to an even healthier April 2014 revision of 4.4%. Dubai's securing of the World Expo 2020 and the ensuing investment in the country that this will bring, coupled to an aggressively growing property market is making the UAE a strong performer on the global economic stage. The UAE's stability in a politically volatile region also contributes to the economic wealth, as foreign companies looking to expand into the region continue to look to the safe havens of Dubai and Abu Dhabi.

There's more good news for those looking to start a business or invest in the UAE too. The MSCI Emerging Markets Index altered the status of the UAE from 'frontier market' to 'emerging market' in mid-2014 on the basis of its stocks performance. That essentially moves the UAE from a risky proposition and into the same league as countries like China and Brazil in the opinion of MSCI. An upgrade of status by an institution such as this instantly has more investors eagerly looking at the country, something highlighted by the fact there is around 100 times more money invested in those markets that mirror MSCI's Emerging Markets Index compared to those in its Frontier Markets Index. While it may take some time for this to bear fruit in the way it's expected, the performance of Abu Dhabi and Dubai's stock exchanges continue to be impressive, with Dubai registering a 200% gain since the beginning of 2013 to become the world's best performing financial market.

Longer term, the UAE is looking to diversify its economy to be less reliant on the oil and gas sector. The government has a strategy called Vision 2021, which highlights the paths to achieving this. There are three main objectives within Vision 2021. Firstly is the desire to increase the productivity of the Emirati population through education and training so that UAE nationals can take the country forward. However, the government points out the continued desire to bring the best people from across the world into the UAE to help drive the economy.

The second objective of Vision 2021 is to boost investment in science, technology, research and development, to increase productivity and competitiveness as the economy becomes

Dubai International Financial Centre

more knowledge-based. Digital infrastructure and more efficient methods of dealing with regulations and government frameworks will be forged to help boost the entrepreneurial aspirations of the country.

And finally, is the plan to establish a sustainable and diversified economy. Not only does this mean taking strides in renewable and sustainable energy sources (and incorporating these into future infrastructure), but it also means looking beyond traditional economic models to ensure the UAE is more flexible and can readily adapt and evolve according to what's happening on the global stage. This also means channelling efforts into sectors that are believed to give the UAE long-term competitive advantages away from oil, many of which will involve the forging of ever-stronger international relations.

Continually, the UAE revises its rules and regulations to balance the needs of its own people while maintaining the attractiveness of the country to foreign workers and investors. For anybody looking to work or set up business here that's a good thing, as for the foreseeable future an expat workforce and the expertise from foreign countries is going to remain integral to the country's development.

DIGITAL INFRASTRUCTURE AND MORE EFFICIENT METHODS OF DEALING WITH REGULATIONS AND GOVERNMENT FRAMEWORKS WILL BE FORGED TO HELP BOOST THE ENTREPRENEURIAL ASPIRATIONS OF THE COUNTRY

KEY INDUSTRIES

The UAE's industry boomed thanks to the discovery of oil, yet its location as a bridge between east and west had already seen the country benefit through trade and re-exports. Today, there's a general realisation that the economy needs to diversify even further in order to avoid dependence on petrochemicals, and it's fair to say that this is already proving successful.

Oil & Gas

There can be no talk of UAE business without a mention of oil and gas. While other sectors are expanding, the petroleum industry remains the backbone of the economy. The Gulf region in general holds a significant proportion of the world's known oil and gas reserves, with the UAE alone sitting on over 97 billion tonnes of proven oil reserves, the seventh largest amount of any country in the world.

With increasing demand from the emerging markets in particular, the prospects for future growth are bright. The demand for natural gas continues to increase as an alternative to oil, which again puts the UAE in a strong position as it has the seventh largest known reserves (with Abu Dhabi accounting for 94% of that).

High-Margin Growth Sectors

Several GCC hydrocarbon-producing countries are looking to monetise a greater portion of their energy reserves by growing

The petroleum industry is central to the UAE's economy

their petrochemical and refining sectors. These higher margin segments of the energy value chain are seeing considerable investment, with Abu Dhabi expanding its energy intensive industries such as aluminium smelting and steel production.

Banking & Finance

Historically, before oil, the UAE's wealth and strength is in trading, so perhaps it should be no surprise that the region has emerged as a regional banking and finance hub. While the petroleum industry remains the biggest contributor to wealth, financial services are also becoming an increasingly important part of the economy. Although trading volumes still remain much lower than in global financial centres like London or New York, when it comes to capital markets or securities trading and asset management, banks within the UAE are among the fastest growing in the world.

The UAE alone now has more than 50 different banking groups, and Dubai has big plans to become the leading regional service and trading centre, although the emirate faces competition from Abu Dhabi and local competition such as Qatar. According to Bloomberg, the stock trading markets in Abu Dhabi and Dubai are amongst the top 10 performers in the last year, with the Abu Dhabi Securities Exchange General Index climbing 40.3% this year, while the Dubai Financial Market General Index has jumped 47.8% in the same period.

Islamic Finance

The Islamic finance sector represents a key growth area in the UAE banking and finance industries as there is a global market. Islamic finance is compliant with Shariah law and essentially instigates longer term relationships between customer and bank, with a shared responsibility to pay the debt and, by nature, lower risks. Mortgages, for example, work on either the customer leasing back the property from the bank, or agreeing a higher than market valuation with the bank, so the extra money paid back over the term is the reward for the bank's risk. Islamic finance also prohibits any dealings with products such as pork, non-halal meat, alcohol, pornography and gambling.

The UAE is well-placed to emerge as a global hub for Shariah-compliant finance as the rapidly growing Muslim populations continue to seek savings and banking products that cater to the sensitivities of the religion. The UAE is currently ranked fifth in the table of leadership and involvement of Islamic finance, as compiled in the 2012 Global Islamic Finance Report, with opportunities to expand into western markets.

HISTORICALLY, BEFORE OIL, THE UAE'S WEALTH AND STRENGTH IS IN TRADING, SO PERHAPS IT SHOULD BE NO SURPRISE THAT THE REGION HAS EMERGED AS A REGIONAL BANKING AND FINANCE HUB

Construction

The construction sector was one of the worst hit industries across the UAE when the financial crisis struck in 2009; however, it remains a multibillion dollar business with significant prospects for future growth.

In Abu Dhabi, once stalled projects have now been reignited, with huge residential and commercial developments in Raha Beach, Khalifa City and Reem Island well underway, to name just a few. The Zayed City area of Abu Dhabi is a project that will create another city within the capital, and is part of a larger plan outlined in the Abu Dhabi government's Abu Dhabi Vision 2030. In Dubai, an ambitious canal project, a mega mall expected to take 10 years to complete, further expansion to the west and the infrastructure for the World Expo 2020, are among developments sure to keep construction booming.

Hospitality & Tourism

Travel and tourism have emerged as increasingly significant contributors to the UAE's economy. Dubai is a shining example of a self-created tourism destination, and its model is being replicated around the Gulf to various degrees.

The country shows no signs of slowing down in this area either with Dubai Chamber of Commerce & Industry forecasting an annual growth rate for tourism in the UAE of 4.1%, culminating in the creation of 245,000 new jobs in the sector by 2023.

Spend, Spend, Spend

TripAdvisor's Cities Survey ranked Dubai best in world for hotels and shopping, beating London and New York. Millions of tourists flock to the UAE each year to spend their cash in its malls – and the lucrative retail sector is only growing.

According to the World Economic Forum's Travel & Tourism Competitiveness Report 2013, the UAE ranked 28th of 139 countries and the first in the Middle East. Dubai takes the lead with a 66% share of the UAE's tourism economy, Abu Dhabi 16% and Sharjah 10%. These all showed strong gains in visitor numbers during 2013 too, with a number of new luxury hotels opening up throughout the UAE in the last 18 months.

Aviation

The UAE's central location between east and west offers a strategic advantage for the locally based aviation industry. Massive investment in the sector continues to create significant employment opportunities in several cities, as the government's efforts to develop world-class airlines and transit hubs advance.

In 2013, Emirates Airline placed the largest ever request for civilian aircraft, with 150 Boeing 777X craft and a further 50 Airbus A380 ordered. At Abu Dhabi International Airport, the huge Midfield Extension is expected to increase annual air traffic by 20 million passengers upon completion in 2017.

Healthcare

The healthcare sector relies heavily on expat staff at all levels and, with growing healthcare spend, the prospects for employment opportunities remain bright. The country's federal diversification plan, UAE Vision 2021, outlines the strategy to continue to invest and partner with best-in-class companies to build a first-rate healthcare infrastructure, while growing expertise and services to fulfil its citizens' needs and expectations.

By 2015, the UAE government expects annual expenditure to reach Dhs.40 million. There's also a push for increasing medical tourism throughout the country, but particularly in Dubai, which aims to become known as a global centre of medical excellence.

Trade & Logistics

The UAE's central location between Europe and Asia, and increasingly active trade links with the rapidly expanding Asian economies, position it advantageously for import and export traders. Dubai is currently the third largest export hub in the world, after Shanghai and Hong Kong, with an almost unheard of four-hour transit from plane to ship of cargo goods. Currently Japan, India, Iran, South Korea and Thailand are the major export destinations for UAE goods, but the re-export of goods from across the world contributes significantly to the sector.

Conversely, the UAE is India's largest export market, accounting for just over 10% of total merchandise exports. The UAE is forecast to maintain this position to 2030 due to robust demand growth. Important Indian exports to the UAE include gems and jewellery, electronics, fabrics, machinery and equipment. India also uses the UAE as a gateway to other markets in the region.

Other Industries

As the UAE looks to expand its economy to rely less on the oil sector, opportunities are opening up all of the time. Already, the retail and fast-moving consumer goods (FMCG) sectors, as well as telecommunications, IT, media, education, manufacturing, recruitment and advertising, are among the industries seeking skilled and qualified professionals in the UAE, with most of those sectors already well-established.

AS THE UAE LOOKS TO EXPAND ITS ECONOMY TO RELY LESS ON THE OIL SECTOR, OPPORTUNITIES ARE OPENING UP ALL OF THE TIME

EXPAT
LIFE

THE UAE MANAGES WHAT SOME ARAB COUNTRIES FAIL TO ACHIEVE: A HEALTHY BALANCE BETWEEN WESTERN INFLUENCES AND EASTERN TRADITIONS

EXPATS ACCOUNT FOR OVER

80%

OF THE POPULATION

DUBAI IS WELL AND TRULY POSITIONING ITSELF AS THE RETAIL CAPITAL OF THE WORLD

Moving to the United Arab Emirates is likely to be one of the easiest relocations abroad that you can make. The whole country, especially the urban hubs of Abu Dhabi and Dubai, is set up to accommodate expats, with a high foreign workforce forming the backbone of the country's economy. No matter what nationality you are, you're likely to find plenty of your countrymen here, as well as other nationalities eager to mix with new people.

Local Population

The number of foreigners living here accounts for over 80% of the population, with the native Emirati now in the minority. This is particularly true in Dubai, where expats account for closer to 85% of the population. However, while the UAE government welcomes both skilled and manual workers from across the world, it also makes great efforts to ensure the indigenous population is not marginalised. Emiratis are afforded certain privileges over expats (such as the ability to own property in all areas, the right to sponsor companies, job opportunities through Emiratisation etc) and the national religion of Islam is adhered to strictly.

Working Life

One of the big incentives is the tax-free salaries, which can leave a lot of disposable income at the end of the month compared to pay packets back home. But be warned, the readily accessible selection of big engine cars, luxurious restaurants and temptation of five-star breaks at the country's excellent resorts and in the nearby region can soon see that disappear.

On a day-to-day level, it's likely you'll have a similar routine to the one you had at home. Working days are generally from 9am to 6pm, although some government companies start at around 7.30am and finish at 2.30pm. During the holy month of Ramadan, working hours are also reduced, usually finishing a few hours earlier then usual.

Education

You will need to enrol your child in a private school. Although prices can be high, your child will learn Arabic and other languages from a young age, the facilities are world-class, and schools are a melting pot of nationalities.

Schools generally start at 8am and finish at 1pm or 3pm, so if both parents are working, a nanny or reliable friend may be needed in order to pick them up and take them home. Many schools run plenty of after-school clubs that can help, too.

NO MATTER WHAT NATIONALITY YOU ARE, YOU'RE LIKELY TO FIND PLENTY OF YOUR COUNTRYMEN HERE, AS WELL AS OTHER NATIONALITIES EAGER TO MIX WITH NEW PEOPLE

TEN REASONS
TO MOVE TO THE UAE

1. **It's ready-made for outside living** Sunshine all year. There are more than 850 hectares of parks and in excess of 22,500 hectares of conservation areas, plus over 10 Blue Flag beaches to lounge on.
2. **High standard of living** Spacious villa/apartment lifestyle, with private/shared pool in the garden. Live-in nanny or maid an affordable option. Access to world-class restaurants, attractions and hotels.
3. **It's all about the money, money, money** Competitive, tax-free salaries. Expat packages including housing, education and health allowances, if you're lucky. Cheap-as-chips fuel.
4. **Very low crime rate** It's a safe place to raise a family.
5. **It's a melting pot of old and new** Middle Eastern traditions are well and truly alive in the local food, architecture, dress and museums. Where else can you watch camel racing and the international golf and tennis in one weekend?
6. **Access to world-class education** Highly rated private schools and universities.
7. **Developing arts and cultural centre** Dubai will be home to the Dubai Modern Art Museum and Opera House District, while Abu Dhabi is getting a Guggenheim and a Louvre – it doesn't get artier than that. International superstars, the likes of Bruno Mars, The Killers and Florence and the Machine, come to town – and you can actually get tickets!
8. **Meet and work with many nationalities** Explore new cuisines and learn about different cultures.
9. **You 're at the centre of everything – literally** It's only a 30-minute drive at most to any attraction, restaurant or beach from home. UAE airports are less than a five-hour flight away from Goa, the Seychelles, parts of Africa and Europe, and the Maldives.
10. **It's the future** Forward-thinking companies. Fast-developing landscape. Growing economy.

REALLY TAX FREE?
Yes and no. You don't pay income or sales tax, except when you purchase alcohol from a licensed liquor store – when you'll be hit with a steep 30% tax. The main tax that you will come across is the municipality tax of 5% on rent, and 10% on food, beverages and hotels. The rest are hidden taxes in the form of 'fees', such as visa/permit fees and Dubai's Salik (road toll).

Healthcare

Both private and public healthcare services are available in the UAE, with English speaking staff and internationally-trained medics in most facilities. Employers must provide private health insurance for all employees which gives you access to a network of private hospitals and clinics. Levels of cover vary depending on the policy; dental care, maternity and screening tests aren't usually covered as standard.

THE UAE HAS MORE THAN 850 HECTARES OF PARKS AND MORE THAN 10 BLUE FLAG BEACHES TO LOUNGE ON

Driving

Vehicles in the UAE have the steering wheel on the left and driving is on the right hand side of the road. If you're used to driving the other way around, don't worry – the vast majority of cars in the UAE have automatic transmissions, which makes it much easier to get used to.

If you have a residence visa then you must have a UAE driving licence – it is illegal to drive without one. Some nationals qualify for an automatic licence transfer: Australia, Austria, Bahrain, Belgium, Canada, Denmark, Finland, France, Germany, Greece, Ireland, Italy, Japan, Kuwait, the Netherlands, New Zealand, Norway, Oman, Poland, Portugal, Qatar, Romania, Saudi Arabia, South Africa, South Korea, Spain, Sweden, Switzerland, Turkey, United Kingdom and the United States. This licence is then valid for 10 years. If you are not eligible for automatic licence transfer, you will have to completely re-sit a theory and practical driving test.

Entertainment

Eating out is a popular pastime in the UAE, namely because there are so many delicious options. With such a varied population of nationalities calling the UAE home, the city's eateries have evolved to cater to a diverse range of palettes. A Friday ritual, the all-you-can-eat (and drink) brunches are infamous in Abu Dhabi and Dubai. They're a perfect place to try everything hotel restaurants can offer, although you may struggle to find room for a taste of it all. At the moment, smoking is banned in some restaurants and bars, but there are still many places where you can light up.

Shopping

Dubai is well and truly positioning itself as the retail capital of the world – and is home to one of the world's largest shopping malls, The Dubai Mall. But it doesn't end there – the UAE's shopping highlights include traditional souks and markets, boutiques, and a growing number of outdoor farmers' markets and artisanal craft fairs.

COST OF LIVING

According to the 2014 Cost of Living survey by the Economist Intelligence Unit (EIU), the UAE's major cities rank relatively low but are slowly rising: Dubai is now 94th of the 131 metropolitan cities listed, while Abu Dhabi ranked 83rd. In real terms, many expats are finding rents and education fees on the upward swing, yet still find they enjoy a higher quality of life in the UAE.

Tax-Free Income

It's always very exciting to hear there is no income tax in the UAE. But it's a mistake to automatically assume salaries here will be the same or higher than back home, with the hefty bonus of no income tax being taken out. Sometimes a tax-free salary package here can be similar to a take-home pay at home.

If an employee, you should also find out what's included in your package. Sometimes the cost of housing, school fees, home help and health insurance for you and your family is included, but not always. It depends on the employer. As a business owner you won't pay any business taxes, but there are plenty of licence fees and charges that can amount to as much.

Housing

Housing is one of the biggest outlays, and in the UAE the cost of renting can vary hugely. The big cities of Dubai and Abu Dhabi are the most expensive places to rent, primarily because these are the major hubs of employment for expats.

Housing in Dubai is of a high standard

In Dubai, rents continue to rise, forcing many to look to places like Sharjah and even as far out as Ras Al Khaimah in order to afford a place large enough for their needs. Abu Dhabi's housing laws demand that employees reside in the emirate in order to claim their housing allowance. Many expats commuting from Dubai have been forced to move to the capital. Coupled with the fact that the Abu Dhabi government removed the 5% cap on rental increase, this could see significant spikes in housing costs here.

Most landlords demand one cheque to pay for rental accommodation. You may be able to negotiate paying in two, four or six cheques at a higher price. In Dubai, a housing fee of 5% of your yearly rent is charged through your Dubai Electricity and Water Authority (DEWA) bill, spread across 12 months.

AS A BUSINESS OWNER YOU WON'T PAY ANY BUSINESS TAXES, BUT THERE ARE PLENTY OF LICENCE FEES AND CHARGES THAT CAN AMOUNT TO AS MUCH

Maids & Nannies

Having full-time or live-in home help may be something most of us could never have dreamed of back home. But many expats find the cost of a nanny or maid is affordable in the UAE. Embassies publish suggested minimum monthly salaries which start at Dhs.750 a month for Bangladeshis. But it is recommended that you pay a full-time, live-in maid Dhs.2,000 to Dhs.3,000 per month, plus a small allowance for food, clothes and toiletries as they send their money home to pay for the basics for their extended family. You'll also need to cover their flight home at least every two years, and a 'maid tax' of around Dh.5,200 a year. Be aware that you'll be legally responsible for someone you sponsor. It's also now compulsory for sponsors to provide domestic workers with basic private health insurance.

Transport Costs

The good news is that taxis are cheap and readily available in the urban areas of the UAE. A 15-minute journey comes in at around Dhs.25 in Abu Dhabi. Likewise, taking a bus is extremely affordable, with inner city fares just Dhs.2 in the capital, while Dubai's buses and metro will cost you between Dhs.2 and Dhs.7 per journey depending on the type of card you purchase.

Renting A Car

Many new arrivals choose to rent a car, and it's worth haggling over prices as rental companies will negotiate. For an older saloon-type car you can find deals starting at Dhs.1,300 per month if you commit to six months or more. Renting a new family-sized saloon will set you back about Dhs.1,800 monthly. Make sure you opt for the best insurance package you can to help put your mind at ease when you find new dents along the side from inconsiderate door-openers in neighbouring parking spaces.

Buying A Car

If you've always dreamed of owning an expensive sports car or 4WD, living in the UAE might be your opportunity to finally buy one. Many expats find the cost of cars is much lower in the UAE than in their home country and there's a culture of buying brand new cars due to not only the price, but a belief that they get worn out quickly as people drive everywhere. Try test driving one of the latest sports models or 4WDs at one of the numerous dealerships dotted throughout the country's cities. You'll also find good quality second-hand cars with low mileage being sold by expats who are packing up and moving on.

Petrol

An added bonus is that fuel is extremely affordable and it generally costs no more than Dhs.100 for a full tank in a mid-range family car. A Jeep Liberty 4WD costs about Dh.120 to fill up, a Mazda 2 hatchback about Dhs.60 – and don't forget to tip the petrol pump attendant.

Food & Drink

Depending on your tastes, eating out can be cheap as chips if you visit some of the authentic eateries in the UAE. Restaurants and cafes on back streets or in smaller towns often offer

One of many waterfront eateries

incredible value, especially as hotels add additional taxes to their already high prices. However, you can fork out for a Michelin star level meal at one of the country's many posh restaurants and luxury hotels and eat some very fine food indeed. Every weekend, many restaurants offer an all-you-can-eat-and-drink 'brunch' (usually around 12 noon to 4pm, so it's actually lunch) for a fixed price. It's a good way to dine out cheaply as the deals begin at around Dhs.150 per person. Alcohol is taxed and it can cost as much as Dhs.50 for a pint of beer.

IF YOU'VE ALWAYS DREAMED OF OWNING AN EXPENSIVE SPORTS CAR OR 4WD, LIVING IN THE UAE MIGHT BE YOUR OPPORTUNITY TO FINALLY BUY ONE

As with restaurants, supermarkets also vary – the most affordable include LuLu Hypermarket, Carrefour and the Union Co-operative Society, and many local shops sell the essentials at lower prices still. More upscale stores include Spinneys, Choithrams and Waitrose. Much of the fruit and veg, as well as familiar branded goods, are imported and so cost slightly more, or significantly more in some cases, than local produce, but other groceries are comparable in price to what you are used to. A family of four will need around Dhs.2,400 to buy monthly groceries.

Education

If you have school-age children there will also be school fees to pay which can vary greatly. Private education doesn't come cheap. If you're lucky, your company may offer school fees as part of your package. For a good school you can expect to pay Dhs.25,000 plus per year for the kindergarten years, rising to as much as Dhs.60,000 per year for secondary school. On top of this you will usually need to pay around Dhs.500 to put your child's name on a school's waiting list, and a registration fee (around Dhs.2,000), which comes off your fees.

Health Insurance

Health insurance costs in the UAE are estimated to have shot up in the past few years. Comprehensive health insurance can cost about Dhs.180 a month. Without insurance, a medical consultation may cost around Dhs.150, or Dhs.300 at night. Employers are legally required to provide basic medical insurance for employees, but you may want to upgrade your plan for increased coverage.

Utilities

The UAE has just two telecommunications providers, Etisalat and du, so market prices are high for internet, TV and phone. Some major roads in Dubai also charge Salik – a road toll.

Additional Costs: Trips Back Home

Consider also the expense of travelling back home to visit family and friends. Most employers provide one flight home per year for expat employees, but the whole family is not always covered.

CULTURE

The UAE has a balance of many cultures and traditions from across the globe. It is still a country very much rooted in Islamic culture; however, the country's effort to become modern and cosmopolitan is highlighted by an open-minded and liberal outlook.

Religion

Islam is the official religion of the UAE, and is widely practised throughout the country. The Islamic holy day is Friday. Muslims are required to pray five times a day (facing Mecca), and times vary according to the sun. Most people pray at a mosque, but it's not unusual to see people kneeling by the side of the road if they are not near a place of worship. The modern-day call to prayer, transmitted through loudspeakers on the minarets, ensures that everyone knows it's time to pray.

Islam is the principal religion, but the UAE is tolerant of other denominations; the ruling family has, in the past, donated land for the building of churches. There is a vibrant Christian community in Dubai and there is a Hindu temple.

Dos & Don'ts

You'll find that, in general, people in the UAE are patient when it comes to cultural etiquette and are keen to explain their customs to you. However, there are a few cultural dos and don'ts

Sheikh Zayed Grand Mosque, Abu Dhabi

USEFUL ARABIC PHRASES

English	Arabic
yes	na'am
no	la
please	min fadlak (m) min fadlik (f)
thank you	shukran
please (in offering)	tafaddal (m) tafaddali (f)
God willing	in shaa'a l-laah
hello (in reply)	marhabtayn
how are you?	kayf haalak (m) kayf haalik (f)
fine, thank you	zayn shukran (m) zayna shukran (f)
welcome	ahlan wa sahlan
welcome (in reply)	ahlan fiyk (m) ahlan fiyiki (f)

LANGUAGE
Arabic is the official language of the UAE. However, English is so widely used, including in business, that you might never need to learn a single word of Arabic. That's not to say that learning a few words or phrases isn't a good idea though. If you can throw in a couple of words here and there you're more likely to receive a warmer welcome.

that you should be aware of to avoid causing offence or landing yourself in trouble with the law.

PDAs
Public displays of affection are a no-no in the UAE and anything more than an innocent peck on the cheek will at best earn you disapproving looks from passers-by.

Appropriate Attire
Beach wear on the beach is fine but, in public, dress should be more conservative. Covering shoulders and knees is a safe bet if you are unsure. It's wise for women to carry a pashmina so they can cover up when necessary. That said, pretty much anything goes when out at bars and clubs.

Home Values
When visiting an Emirati house it is customary to remove your shoes. Traditionally men and women dine separately and meals are eaten sat on floor cushions. Be careful when sitting not to point your feet at anyone or show the soles of your feet. Try everything offered at the meal, but if you're not sure you'll like something, just take a small amount. If you invite a Muslim to your home, offering pork or alcohol may cause offence.

Photography
Like anywhere in the Arab world, it is courteous to ask permission before photographing people, particularly women. Photographs of government and military buildings shouldn't be taken, especially if there are 'no photography' signs. Unwitting tourists have found themselves in deep trouble for this before.

Out On The Town

The UAE has a good variety of nightlife and alcohol is widely available in the country's hotel bars, pubs and clubs (except for Sharjah, which is a dry emirate). Remember, however, that you're in a Muslim country and drunken or lewd behaviour is not only disrespectful but can lead to arrest and detention.

Tipping

Tipping is not compulsory, but tipping for good service is common, normally around 10% of your bill. Many restaurants include a 10% service charge although it's unclear how much will find its way into your waiter's pocket, so some people add a little extra. For valet parking at hotels a Dhs.5 tip is average, and taxi fares are usually rounded up to include a tip.

Ramadan

During this important religious period, Muslims will fast during daylight hours, abstaining from food, drink and smoking for one month. Two meals are consumed each night; one before sunrise (suhour) and one after sunset (iftar). As the sun sets each evening, the fast is broken with the iftar prayer. Many restaurants lay out a sumptuous iftar buffet, and non-Muslim residents can also take part in the festivities with friends and family.

DOS & DON'TS

DURING THE HOLY MONTH

- DO consume food in private. Restaurants and coffee shops close during daylight hours in respect of Muslims who are fasting. While many offer a take-away option, you should not eat your food in public.
- DO NOT eat, drink or smoke in public (including inside your car). It is illegal and, if caught, you are likely to pay a fine of up to Dhs.2,500 with harsher punishments stretching to two months in jail.
- DO dress more conservatively during Ramadan.
- DO NOT play loud music (including inside your car). Nightclubs are closed during the holy month, while lounges and bars are likely to respect this rule.
- DO NOT dance in public places during Ramadan as this is seen as disrespectful.
- DO NOT get caught for an alcohol-related offence, including being drunk in public, as these are likely to be treated far harsher during Ramadan.

EID AL FITR

The end of Ramadan is celebrated with an important festival, Eid Al Fitr, which is announced the previous evening according to the sighting of the moon. The public sector will be granted several days off, while the private sector will typically get two days' holiday.

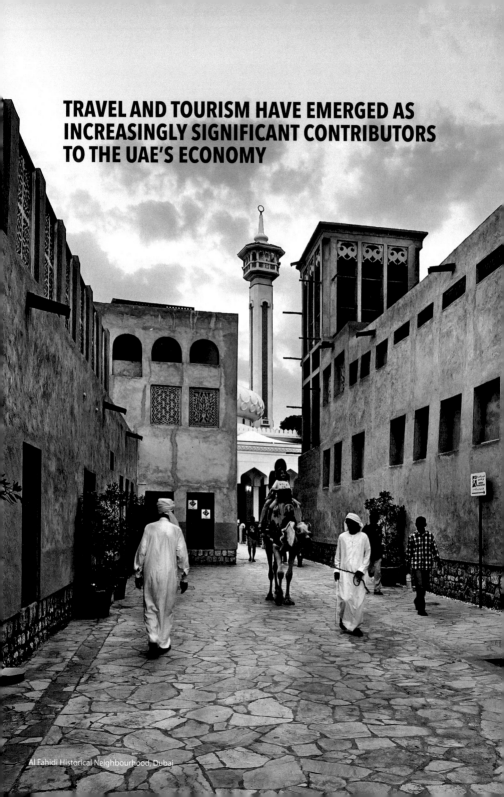

TRAVEL AND TOURISM HAVE EMERGED AS INCREASINGLY SIGNIFICANT CONTRIBUTORS TO THE UAE'S ECONOMY

Al Fahidi Historical Neighbourhood, Dubai

UAE RESIDENCE

To live in the UAE, you need a residence visa, and there are three main types: employment, family and domestic worker. You either need to have a job in the UAE and be sponsored by an employer, or be married to, or related to (son/daughter) someone who has a job here and they will sponsor you.

To enter the UAE you will need a visit visa (see How To... No.18). Once you arrive, you can apply for a residence visa and, as part of the process, you will need to take a medical test and apply for your Resident ID Card (formerly known as Emirates ID). Once you have your visa – and this process can be completed in less than a month – you can legally live and work in the UAE.

After entering the UAE, you have 60 days to complete the visa application process – but it's unlikely to take that long.

The residence visa permits you to live anywhere in the UAE, and you can live and work in different emirates. It is valid for two or three years (depending on where you are working), after which you'll need to re-apply.

Family Residence Visa

If you are a resident in the UAE you should be able to sponsor your family members (wife, husband, children) allowing them to stay in the country as long as you are here, provided you meet the minimum salary requirement of Dhs.4,000 (or Dhs.3,000 with an accommodation allowance).

Follow the same procedure as opposite, but you also need:
- Tenancy contract attested through the relevant municipality department of your emirate of residence
- Marriage and birth certificates (as applicable) attested by the UAE embassy in your home country and the Ministry of Foreign Affairs in the UAE
- Last three months' bank statements. Online printed statements will not be accepted

Resident ID

All expats need to register with the Emirates Identity Authority (EIDA) for a Resident Identity Card before applying for their residence visa. Without the application you won't be able to complete the medical tests required for the visa. Additionally, if you fail to sign up you'll face daily fines of Dhs.20.

Each card contains the holder's address, photo, date of birth and fingerprints, and is an official source of identification. It will eventually replace all other cards, such as health and labour cards, and can already be used at the e-Gate service at the UAE's main airports if the user pays the Dhs.150 activation fee.

1

HOW TO...

PASSPORT PHOTOS

If you need passport photos (and you will need them, taken against a white background and printed on gloss paper), Grand Stores (grandstores.com) has branches throughout the city and can provide the correct size photos. Look out for Kodak outlets in all shopping malls, which can also print passport-sized photos from your own snaps.

APPLY FOR AN EMPLOYMENT RESIDENCE VISA (EMPLOYMENT)

PREREQUISITES
- Aged under 65 years old
- Minimum six months validity on passport
- Have a job offer, be currently employed, or be setting up a business
- Medical completed (and passed) at a health authority centre. You will need to take a blood test (for HIV and other communicable diseases) and a chest x-ray for TB
- Resident Identity Card application is underway

PROCEDURE
WHERE: General Directorate of Residency and Foreigners' Affairs (GDRFA)
Submit the following:
- Passport (original)
- Resident ID application form certified by the EIDA
- Entry permit or visit visa stamp
- Medical test certificate
- Attested education certificates
- Company's establishment immigration card & trade licence
- Five passport-sized photos
- Fees: Dhs.310 fee (plus typing fees)

Reading a good book is like taking a journey

Your fondest memories are probably the ones where you've curled up with a good book and los
yourself in its world. For children, a book is more than just a tool, it is a gateway to a magical
place where learning and wonderment go hand in hand. Give your child the perfect start in lif
with our excellent selection of childrens' books.

Mall of the Emirates 04 3406789 • Selected Spinneys Supermarkets

SETTING UP A BUSINESS

THE
OPTIONS

THE UAE AS A WHOLE IS CONSIDERED A PLACE WHERE YOU CAN DO BUSINESS WITH MINIMAL RED TAPE. IT ALSO OPERATES A ZERO INCOME TAX AND CORPORATE TAX POLICY

A UAE NATIONAL SPONSOR HAS A
51%
STAKE IN A MAINLAND BUSINESS

FULL PRIVATE FOREIGN OWNERSHIP IS PERMITTED WITHIN FREE ZONES

Setting up a business in the UAE can certainly appear daunting. There's a raft of bureaucracy to deal with and some idiosyncrasies that can catch out the unaware, although, in truth, these are no less arduous than in many other countries around the world. The UAE is a thriving market and the rewards for establishing a successful business here can be large, so the initial pain of getting your idea up and running is worth it in the long term.

The reasons for setting up in the UAE include the stable nature of the country in a strategic region that joins east with west, yet is beset with political and social turmoil. The lack of taxation and the fact that the population continues to boom, many of them with considerable disposable income, are also key factors. Today, all of that remains true, but the country and its business environment is still developing, and that means there are niches and gaps in the market that are crying out to be filled.

THE COUNTRY AND ITS BUSINESS ENVIRONMENT IS STILL DEVELOPING, AND THAT MEANS THERE ARE NICHES AND GAPS IN THE MARKET THAT ARE CRYING OUT TO BE FILLED

Where to start?

There are two jurisdictions in the UAE for conducting business: the 'mainland', and more than 30 free trade zones, which offer different advantages depending on your business activities. Wherever you decide to set up, you will not have to pay any business or personal taxes. You will, however, face certain annual licence fees and charges that may take you by surprise.

Mainland

All companies setting up outside a free zone must have a trade licence that determines which business activities you are permitted to practise. You must also have either:

- sponsorship from a UAE national, who will have a 51% stake in your business (if setting up a limited liability company (LLC) or public/private shareholding company) **OR**
- sponsorship from a local service agent (if setting up a branch company, sole proprietorship or civil business)

Free Trade Zones

Free zones have their own set of rules and procedures for establishing a company, and are designed to encourage foreign investment. The rules and procedures differ from the mainland, particularly with regards to foreign ownership.

For example, a branch or a representative office can be established in a free zone with the support of the free zone authority. Non-nationals and foreign companies may also choose to set up a free zone branch as their head office. Full private foreign ownership is permitted, albeit with significant annual fees.

THE COUNTRY HAS SEEN A MAJOR SME PUSH OF LATE, AS BANKS WORK TO OFFER BETTER DEALS FOR SMALLER FIRMS AND LOCAL GOVERNMENTS STAGE SME NETWORKING, RECOGNITION, AND EDUCATION EVENTS

Helping Hand

The bureaucracy of getting a business off the ground can put people off from carrying out their great ideas. Fortunately, the government appears to realise this and, as private enterprise is a key way for the UAE's economy to become more diverse, there are measures being put in place that should help make entrepreneurs feel more empowered to take the plunge.

The country has seen a major SME push of late, as banks work to offer better deals for smaller firms and local governments stage SME networking, recognition, and education events. In the run up to Dubai Expo 2020, there is a palpable grassroots entrepreneurial push. Popular SME support hubs continue to thrive, such as Impact Hub, based in Downtown Dubai or Jumeirah Beach Residence's MAKE Business Hub. In Abu Dhabi, the Abu Dhabi Business Centre (adbc.abudhabi.ae) is currently being created. This will be a 'one-stop shop' for budding business owners, where 15 of the different government agencies that a new start-up might need will be housed under one roof. By the end of 2014 the doors to the Business Centre should be open and at least provide a focal point for any new business in the emirate.

In Dubai, the Department of Economy has launched a system that allows entrepreneurs to be in business within hours of completing an online form. By using My ID – an online government portal – they can complete a memorandum of association form and then start trading, with a 120-day grace period in which to complete all of the other necessary paperwork. It means not only a quick start-up, but also added convenience in that partners in a business can complete this initial procedure remotely, rather than having to go somewhere together. Once completed, a copy of their trade licence will be sent to their smartphone and from that point they're ready to go. However, some businesses such as restaurants or those in the medical profession are excluded from this new system, as public health risks deem extended checks necessary.

The UAE government is also drafting new laws that will help to not only make business set-up a little more tempting, but also address some of the concerns raised in the past. For example, the issue of bankruptcy and the fact there is no government-structured method to resolving the issue when companies fail, is being revised. The new laws should mean entrepreneurs have a more certain prospect of resolution should the company they start fail, and their creditors will also benefit too. Clearly these moves are all positive steps for the UAE's economy, and good news for anybody looking to start a business in the country.

GETTING STARTED

Ask most UAE entrepreneurs and they will recommend using a business set-up company for at least part of the initial process.

Throughout this chapter you find all the information you need to know about choosing your trade licence, deciding where to set up, and the processes and procedures involved. You are likely to find, however, that it's never as simple as it may seem, and the help of a business set-up company can ease a lot of headaches, save a lot of time, and free you up to concentrate on the running of your business.

There are plenty of business set-up companies in the UAE, with years of experience in helping businesses get off the ground. These companies are well-connected within the industry and with the government departments needed in the process. They can offer services for part or all of the process, from finding a UAE national sponsor to getting your trade licence, as well as guidance when it comes to weighing up all the set-up options for your commercial activities.

Legal Advice

To fully understand the benefits and limitations of each set-up option in relation to your business plan, it is recommended to gather legal advice from trusted sources. There's plenty to consider with regard to the restrictions of each company type, and it's important to plan for issues that may arise further down the line.

UAE Business Set-up Companies

Al Taresh Consultants & Services 04 266 6345, *altaresh.com*
BTMS Consultancy 04 422 1296, *bahriatown.com*
Business Setup Consultants 04 430 1245, *businesssetup.com*
Cosmohub Management Consultancy Services 02 650 8412, *cosmohub.ae*
Creative Zone 04 455 8455, *creativezone.ae*
Index Group 02 626 5181, *indexdubai.com*
Intuit Management Consultancy 04 370 9963, *intuitconsultancy.com*
Emirates Business & Management Consultant 04 208 7800, *ebmconsultant.com*
Enjazat Services 02 666 6319, *enjazat.ae*
Key Business Group 04 239 7779, *keybusiness.ae*
Links Group of Companies 04 446 3900, *linksgroup.com*
One Stop Management Consultancy 04 332 2256, *onestopdubai.com*
Plus UAE 02 491 9050, *plusuae.com*
Ultimate Business Setup 04 425 3088, *theultimate.ae*
Victory Venture 04 451 7788, *victoryventure.com*
World Wide Formations 04 304 2600, *worldwideformations.com*

YOUR OPTIONS

If you're planning on setting up a business in the UAE, there are six main ways to do it. Within each of these, however, there are further options that need consideration. The six main types of business set-up are outlined here. Later in this chapter you will find a step-by-step guide to each of the set-up options.

To set up outside of a free zone, you will need to either have sponsorship from a UAE national sponsor or sign a Local Service Agreement with a local service agent.

UAE National Sponsor

If setting up an LLC or a public or private shareholding company, you will need the sponsorship of a UAE national or UAE-owned company, who holds 51% of the shares in your company. This national sponsor acts only as the local sponsor to obtain and renew the licences, visas and work permits relating to the company and its employees. They will not necessarily take 51% of the profits, and many companies enter into a 'side agreement' with the sponsor where a percentage is agreed. This will need to be renewed annually in line with your trade licence.

You will need to draw up a Local Agency Agreement with the sponsor to submit for the full trade licence, and agree on the terms of the partnership in the company's MOA. There are companies that can find you a sponsor, such as Links Group

It is easy to find a local sponsor for your business

UAE Business Guide

(linksgroup.com), which can also draw up the agreement and even take care of all administration so that you don't necessarily need to deal directly with the sponsor.

However, a sponsor is not needed for some companies in specific industries such as oil and gas, and global banks are also exempt. Alternatively, a local service agent, which is similar to a sponsor but has no stake in the business and works for a fixed fee, is needed for any sole proprietorship, civil business or branch office.

Local Service Agent

If setting up a branch company, sole proprietorship or civil business, you will need to sign a Local Service Agreement, detailing the relationship and the obligations of the owner and the agreement; it must be authenticated by a notary public within the UAE. This needs to be arranged before applying for the full trade licence.

A local service agent does not undertake any financial obligations concerning the activities of the company's branch or office within the UAE or abroad, and does not get involved in business matters. Their role is confined to providing such services as: obtaining of visit/residence visa, acquiring of the necessary licences, and facilitating the processing of transactions with the government authorities. The local service agent is remunerated with a lump sum amount, the subject of an agreement between him and the company.

Legal Forms

If setting up a mainland business, you will need to select one of the following legal forms:

1. A permanent establishment
2. A branch office
3. A professional/civil company (currently only in Dubai and Sharjah)
4. Sole proprietorship
5. Commercial agency agreement

The sixth option is to set up in a free zone, and there's plenty of information on this later in the chapter.

1. Permanent Establishment

A permanent establishment is essentially a company or partnership created in the UAE, rather than being a branch office or a free zone entity. The options for this are as follows:

IF SETTING UP AN LLC OR A PUBLIC OR PRIVATE SHAREHOLDING COMPANY, YOU WILL NEED THE SPONSORSHIP OF A UAE NATIONAL OR UAE-OWNED COMPANY, WHO HOLDS 51% OF THE SHARES IN YOUR COMPANY

Limited Liability Company (LLC)

An LLC is a hybrid of a partnership and a corporation. Its owners are shielded from personal liability; the liability of the shareholders is limited to their shares in the company's capital and selling shares publicly is not permitted. Formed by a minimum of two and a maximum of 50 people, an LLC is a popular choice for anyone setting up a company outside of a free zone in the UAE, because it's possible for foreign ownership to exert significant control. While an Emirati sponsor is required, an LLC can add provisions within its constitutional documents allowing for the foreign shareholder to appoint all directors, appoint the general manager, veto major decisions of the company, be entitled to all assets when winding up the company and, crucially, to be entitled to more than 49% of the company's profits. For those setting up an offshore company in the UAE, LLC status is also required. Summary of requirements:

- Sponsorship from a UAE national, who must have a 51% stake in your business
- Company auditor must be UAE accredited
- Trade name (ending with 'LLC') must be approved by appropriate economic department of the emirate

Public/Private Shareholding Company

Shareholding companies are primarily set up for large projects or operations, since the minimum capital required is Dhs.10 million for a public company, and Dhs.2 million for a private company. Companies engaging in banking, insurance, or financial activities should be run as public shareholding companies. The chairman and majority of directors must be UAE nationals. Sponsorship from a UAE national, who must have a 51% stake in your business, is required.

IF SETTING UP A BRANCH COMPANY, SOLE PROPRIETORSHIP OR CIVIL BUSINESS, YOU WILL NEED TO SIGN A LOCAL SERVICE AGREEMENT, DETAILING THE RELATIONSHIP AND THE OBLIGATIONS OF THE OWNER AND THE AGREEMENT

General Partnerships

A general partnership may be established between two or more general partners who are jointly and unlimitedly, to the extent of their personal assets, responsible for the company's liabilities. Only UAE nationals can form a general partnership.

Limited Partnerships

A limited partnership has at least one general partner and at least one limited partner, essentially an active (general) and silent (limited) partner. The former has obligations to the full extent of their assets, while the latter's obligations are limited to their capital contributions. Only UAE nationals can be general partners, while nationals from any country can be limited partners.

JLT, Dubai

Joint Participation (Ventures)

Also known as a private unlimited company, this is an association between at least two partners who will share the profit and loss in one or more commercial businesses conducted by one of the partners in his or her own name. This is often the best course of action when undertaking specific projects and is a good way of working with a UAE-based company.

Sponsorship from a UAE national, who must have a 51% stake in your business, is required. There's no need to licence the joint venture or publish the agreement.

2. Branch Office

A foreign company can set up a branch office either within or outside a free zone. The parent company remains responsible for all the liabilities and financial obligations of the branch office. This may have tax implications in the country of origin of the parent company; any revenue generated by the branch would generally constitute a part of the revenues generated by the parent company. The branch office of a foreign company carries out activities similar to that of its parent company subject to the approval of the economic department of the emirate it's in. See overleaf for a summary of requirements.

- Appoint a local service agent if outside a free zone
- Branch must engage in similar activities to parent company
- Trade name must be the same name as the parent company
- Parent company must have been registered for two years in home country
- Branch must not import parent company products
- Bank guarantee of Dhs.50,000 required

Alternatively, a representative/liaison office is limited to promoting its parent company's activities. This means that a representative office is only permitted to perform such activities as gathering information, soliciting orders, and marketing projects to be performed by the company's head office. This type of office is also limited in the number of employees that they sponsor.

3. Professional/Civil Company

Also referred to as a business partnership, professional business or consultancy, this type of company falls under the civil code, rather than commercial, and is unique to the UAE. Companies can engage in professional or artisan activities but the number of staff members will be limited. 100% foreign ownership, sole proprietorships or civil companies are permitted. Must appoint a local service agent if outside a free zone.

4. Sole Proprietorship

This is the most basic form of business, and can only be owned by an individual, not a company. This person will own 100% of the business, control all of its operations and keep 100% of any profits. He or she will also be 100% responsible for business debts and any other financial obligations. Non-GCC nationals are not permitted to own an industrial or commercial business. In effect, it is for individuals offering a service such as architecture or management consultancy and their trade licence is in their own name. Owner must practise the activity on his/her own. Must appoint a local service agent if outside a free zone.

5. Commercial Agency Agreement

This is only of consideration if you want to carry out business in the UAE but not have a physical presence. By appointing a commercial agent, either a UAE national or wholly local owned entity, you can have them distribute your imported goods in specified locations (at least one emirate) for agreed sales commissions. In an official commercial agency agreement, the products you import must be exclusive, the agent is entitled to commission on any sales in the country that you or anybody else makes, and the Commercial Agencies Committee will need to be involved if you plan on terminating the agreement.

6. Free Zone Entity

Establishing your business within a Free Trade Zone (FTZ) negates the need for a sponsor or local service agent.

Covered in greater depth later in this chapter, the UAE's Free Trade Zones can be one of the easiest ways for foreign companies to establish a presence in the UAE. There are free zones all across the UAE, although the majority are in Dubai, followed by an increasing number in Abu Dhabi.

Each free zone is generally dedicated to specific types of industry so it's a case of setting up in the appropriate one to what your company offers. Each is also autonomously run by its own authority, meaning different rules and regulations are applicable. The benefits to setting up in a free zone are that 100% foreign ownership is allowed, and the company receives 100% repatriation of capital and profits. Free zone companies are still exempt from all corporation and personal income taxes in the UAE too.

However, the limitation is that business can't directly be done with the UAE market without specific additional licences and locally appointed distributors. (See How To... No. 11.)

Offices in the UAE are modern

THE COSTS

Whether you are setting up a mainland business or in a free zone, there are plenty of costs to consider. These can change quickly, so be sure to find out the most up to date information by calling the relevant government department or Free Zone Authority (FZA).

Mainland Business

The cost of a UAE trade licence for a mainland business ranges from Dhs.5,000 to Dhs.200,000 depending on industry and activity. Licence renewal is typically 40-50% of the original cost. Other start-up costs incude establishment immigration and labour cards (Dhs.4,000), company PO Box (Dhs.150), Ministry of Economy fees (Dhs.3,000), plus the endless admin fees, insurance, legal and accountancy, and employee visas. Paid-up capital requirements vary greatly.

Administrative Costs

1. Reserve a company name and apply for registration at the Department of Economic Development (DED)
Time to complete: One day
Cost: Dhs.110 for initial approval and Dhs.210 for name reservation, plus up to Dhs.3,000 name fee

2. Notarise company's Memorandum of Association at DED
Time to complete: One day
Cost: 0.25% of the capital (for three copies of the memorandum of association), Dhs.5 for each page of the additional copy. The maximum notary fee is Dhs.10,000.

3. File company documents with the DED, obtain trade licence and register for membership at the Chamber of Commerce and Industry
Time to complete: Three days
Cost: 5% of the value of the lease agreement, Dhs.1,000-3,000 waste fees, Dhs.480 for company registration, Dhs.350 fees for nameboard, and Dhs.1,200 for Chamber of Commerce membership.

4. Apply for the establishment card at Ministry of Labour
Time to complete: One day
Cost: Dhs.2,000

UAE Free Zones

Free zones often ask for a business plan and the initial capital required can be very high, from Dhs.300,000 - 1 million. Start-up fees normally comprise a one-time registration fee, trade licence fee, rental lease and sundry costs, such as post box rent, card charges, name approval charges and notarisation.

ESTIMATED FREE ZONE START-UP COSTS

Ajman Free Zone Company	from $9,055
Dubai Airport Free Zone Company	from $29,184
Dubai Internet City	from $15,616
DMCC / JLT Free Zone Company	from $17,027
Dubai World Central Free Zone Company	from $11,616
Fujairah Free Zone Company	from $13,528
Hamriyah Free Zone Company	from $10,190
Jebel Ali Free Zone (JAFZA) Company	from $15,773
RAK Free Trade Zone Company	from $9,561
RAKIA Free Zone company	from $9,041
Sharjah Airport Free Zone Company	from $10,718

Source: UAE Company Registration

Open For e-Business

In the past, the UAE's processes for completing the various transactions the government requires in the set-up and running of your business have been accused of being cumbersome and weighed down with red tape. Today, on the contrary, there is a sophisticated and comprehensive portal, particularly in Dubai, where many transactions can be completed simply and painlessly online and through mobile apps. Many of these are free to download.

The iPhone app mDubai allows you, amongst other things, to access information on, and maintain channels of communication with, all Dubai government entities. You can gain information on services related to your business, search for any government service under How To, and centrally access news of all developments within the different Dubai government departments.

Through mPay, for iPhone and Android, you can pay for a number of services such as Dubai Police fines, Dubai Electricity and Water Authority (DEWA) bills, Dubai Roads and Transport Authority (RTA) 'Salik' highway toll charges, and Etisalat mobile, internet, television and landline bills.

Amongst the many other apps are those that provide information on the healthcare system, Dubai Police, Dubai Courts, Public Prosecution and other judicial entities, business and consumer information, and a calendar of the numerous events happening around the city. All can be found, with the full information on what they provide, on dubai.ae.

THE COSTS OF SETTING UP IN A FREE ZONE CAN MOUNT UP. FREE ZONES OFTEN ASK FOR A BUSINESS PLAN AND THE INITIAL CAPITAL REQUIRED CAN BE VERY HIGH

"LOCAL SPONSORSHIP DOES NOT MEAN GIVING UP OWNERSHIP CONTROL"

John Martin St. Valery

Business Links Group
Web linksgroup.ae
Activities Business set-up

John Martin St. Valery is a founding partner of The Links Group. Established in 2002, the company provides services to business setting up in the UAE and Qatar, taking care of all the red tape, from trade licences to finding a local sponsor. It was ranked in the Dubai SME 100.

What are the main factors you should consider when setting up a company in the UAE?
The most important decision is choosing the right legal presence for your business. To conduct business in the UAE on a regular basis, investors are required to establish a legal commercial presence. Currently, investors can set up either in free zones or as onshore entities.

What are the differences between a mainland company and a free zone company? What are the pros and cons of each?
There is a big difference between onshore and free zones. To know which option is best for your business, first ask yourself: 'where is the audience for my company's product or service?'

If the audience is onshore (mainland or outside a free zone), then it would be best to establish an onshore entity, which requires a UAE national to hold a minimum 51% share of the company. But this does not mean giving up ownership control. It is imperative, when setting up a company in the UAE, to protect ownership interests and identify clear succession planning. Nominee partner structures for onshore trade licences, a model which The Links Group pioneered in partnership with Dubai's Foreign Investment Office, do exactly that. The Links Group can also set up an offshore entity to protect the company's 49% shareholding, thereby strengthening beneficial ownership.

If the audience of your business is within a particular free zone or outside of the UAE borders, then free zones offer a great opportunity for foreign investors, such as 100% foreign ownership and tax exemption.

Any Advice?
It is always best to do your due diligence and have a lawyer review your articles or Memoranda of Association so it is prudent to budget for legal fees.

What are the main steps for setting up a mainland company?
The main steps can be outlined as follows:
- Reserve a company name and apply for registration at the Department of Economic Development (DED)
- Notarise the company's Memorandum of Association at the DED
- File company documents with the DED; obtain a trade licence; and register for membership at the Dubai Chamber of Commerce and Industry (DCCI)
- Apply for the establishment card at the Ministry of Labour
- Register native workers with the Ministry of Labour
- Register native workers with the General Authority for Pensions and Social Security

What are the main start-up costs a business will face?
A company will need to have sufficient capital to cover the costs of company incorporation and the associated documentation. This can vary depending on whether the company is established onshore or in a free zone. The cost of incorporating a business onshore in Dubai will vary based on the company type, activity and number of employees.

Most companies in the UAE are required to take physical office space. While businesses will try to start small, it is important to know that employee visa quotas are directly related to the square footage of your office. Each employee requires a minimum of 100 square feet of office space. If recruitment is a priority for you in the first year of operation, you are best to start with a larger office to support this growth.

Are there any ways that companies can keep costs down?
Do not add to your risk burden by making hasty decisions or taking shortcuts when it comes to establishing your business in the correct jurisdiction with the right company incorporation model.

It might also seem quicker and cheaper to set up in a free zone in the UAE. However, by doing so you cannot trade with businesses or consumers based onshore. You would be surprised how often this specific situation occurs, only for the business to find out it is unable to trade where it wants to. It is then saddled with huge costs to unravel their erroneous venture and re-establish their business correctly.

By understanding the regulatory requirements and limitations from the outset, a huge amount of time and money can be saved. While the roadmap may seem complicated, a trusted

A COMPANY WILL NEED TO HAVE SUFFICIENT CAPITAL TO COVER THE COSTS OF COMPANY INCORPORATION AND THE ASSOCIATED DOCUMENTATION

company formation specialist will be able to set you on the right path and help you avoid potentially costly roadblocks along the way.

What are the advantages of setting up a company in the UAE?
The UAE is among the hottest growth destinations in the Middle East. According to the International Monetary Fund (IMF), the UAE's GDP is expected to climb to US$448bn in 2017. Following Dubai's successful bid to host the World Expo 2020, the UAE's economic outlook is expected to remain positive.

There are plenty of opportunities for companies particularly in the construction, retail, food, healthcare, education sector. Beyond this, the UAE has prioritised the growth of its Islamic economy, green technology and hospitality sectors over the next 10 years.

With its pro-business environment, fast-growing economy and geographical proximity to the rest of the world, the UAE presents attractive opportunities for businesses wanting to stimulate their home markets. The UAE is well recognised as a trading hub for the rest of the region and many foreign companies choose to establish a physical presence here.

In addition to robust commercial infrastructure, businesses also benefit from the zero to low corporate tax structures, low custom duties and the ability to repatriate 100 per cent of capital and profits.

What are the challenges of setting up a company in the UAE?
The main challenge is the real estate or property cost associated with process, whether it's renting or purchasing office space. Investors have to consider how to support the business when they plan to set up.

As an expert who has overseen the formation of many companies, what personalised advice can you offer?
There are many routes to setting up a legal commercial presence in the UAE, but not all of them will be able to get your business to where it needs to go. Investors need to take the most appropriate means of legal incorporation to capitalise on the lucrative opportunities the region offers.

Can you recommend any supportive government bodies or private groups for SMEs and company formation?
There is no doubt that Dubai SME, an agency of the Department of Economic Development, is going to great

lengths to support SMEs by offering free valuation advisory services, seminars and workshops.

Dubai FDI, part of the Department of Economic Development in Dubai, provides essential information and invaluable support to foreign businesses looking to invest in Dubai.

Within the UAE there are a number of start-up groups and academies available to support entrepreneurs, such as MAKE Business Hub, Impact Hub Dubai and Heels & Deals.

Also, subscribe to local business publications for access to local know-how. Many of the publications also run events or clinics for SMEs which are particularly useful.

As the first company formation specialist in the UAE to be endorsed by the Government of Dubai through a strategic alliance with Dubai FDI, The Links Group is also a good source of information and expert advice on how to set up a business in the UAE. Our blog provides regular updates on issues affecting UAE-registered companies. Our consultative approach to company formation also means clients discover what process best suits their business.

A TRUSTED COMPANY FORMATION SPECIALIST WILL BE ABLE TO SET YOU ON THE RIGHT PATH AND HELP YOU AVOID POTENTIALLY COSTLY ROADBLOCKS ALONG THE WAY

The Links Group helps businesses get established

WHICH EMIRATE?

Each emirate has something different to offer its start-ups, from unique infrastructure to targeted free zones, population composition to strategic location. It's worth weighing up the different options when it comes to establishing a base for your business – you might not even need a physical office.

Abu Dhabi

According to the most recent World Trade Organisation (WTO) Trade Policy Review for the UAE in 2012, the UAE has crude oil reserves of around 97.8 billion barrels, or almost 8.5% of the world's reserves. Of this, 95% is in Abu Dhabi, the UAE capital, making it one of the world's largest sovereign wealth funds. The Abu Dhabi Statisics Centre cites the capital as contributing around 60% of the UAE's total GDP, while it comprises only 34% of the total population. As a result, says the WTO, production of crude oil and natural gas accounted for 31.6% of the UAE's GDP in 2010.

While energy remains the capital's dominant industry, there are strong moves towards economic diversification, driven by the Abu Dhabi Economic Vision 2030. At the time of formulating its 2030 vision in 2007, Abu Dhabi reported its non-oil GDP at 41%. By 2015 it aims to raise that to 50%, and by 2030 to 64%. That said, because Abu Dhabi's oil sector is predominantly government-controlled, a large proportion of business in the capital comprises government contracts.

The city already has an advanced business infrastructure in terms of commercial office space and communication networks. At the same time, major infrastructural inprovement projects continue. As a result, according to the Abu Dhabi Statistics Centre, construction accounted for 13% of GDP in 2010.

Abu Dhabi's diversification plans have been greatly aided by an increasingly diverse portfolio of free zones. Notably, Masdar City is the first global cleantech cluster dedicated to renewable energy and sustainability technologies, plus a huge research and development arm. Others include Abu Dhabi Airport Free Zone and twofour54, which is dedicated to the media industry.

Dubai

In direct contrast to Abu Dhabi, Dubai holds minimal oil reserves. It does however have the most diversified economy of all the emirates and is home to the regional headquarters of a great number of the world's major multinational firms across a diverse range of business areas. This is within both its 'onshore' locations and free zones.

Unlike Abu Dhabi, which because of its oil-based economy was relatively sheltered from the 2009 crisis, Dubai took a hard economic hit. This was primarily due to its diversified economy, hence exposure to international markets. At the same time, out of all the emirates, Dubai has possibly invested the most into its infrastructure in terms of both business and leisure. As a result, it has seen a robust recovery. According to Dubai Statistics Centre, the emirate saw a GDP growth rate of 7.3% in 2012, compared to 3.9% the year before.

One huge enabler to encouraging foreign direct investment and international talent has been Dubai's emphasis on developing not only its business infrastructure, but also considerable choice in housing, schools, healthcare facilities and recreational options. In this way it has not only positioned itself as a desirable place to work but also to live and raise a family.

A huge source of Dubai's economic growth comes from its import, export and re-export industries. This is partly because of its central global position between east and west, but also because of its sustained efforts to build a logistics infrastructure which has firmly established the emirate as the region's logistics hub – according to the UAE Ministry of Economy, Dubai Customs clears 80% of UAE imports, compared to just 10% in Abu Dhabi. The latest move in this direction is Dubai World Central (DWC), covering an area of 140km2 (almost twice that of Hong Kong Island). Within DWC is Al Maktoum International Airport, the world's largest, which opened in October 2013 with a planned annual capacity of 12 million tonnes of cargo and 160 million passengers. The airport will position Dubai as one of the world's most powerful commerce, logistics and tourism sectors.

A major boost to the Dubai economy has been to secure the World Expo 2020, which it won in November 2013. World Expos offer a global platform to share technological innovation and to move forward in global issues such as sustainability and economic parity. They draw amongst the largest international gatherings of people, and projected visitor figures for Expo 2020 are forecast at 25 million. The six-month event is expected to bring around US$23 billion to the city.

The site for Dubai's World Expo will be 438 hectares of land between Jebel Ali Port and Al Maktoum International Airport (part of the Dubai World Central economic zone currently under construction).

The first emirate to launch the free trade zone concept, Dubai now has a huge network of free zones, including Dubai Media City, Dubai Studio City and Dubai International Financial Centre.

A MAJOR BOOST TO THE DUBAI ECONOMY HAS BEEN TO SECURE THE WORLD EXPO 2020. WORLD EXPOS OFFER A GLOBAL PLATFORM TO SHARE TECHNOLOGICAL INNOVATION AND TO MOVE FORWARD IN GLOBAL ISSUES SUCH AS SUSTAINABILITY AND ECONOMIC PARITY

Sharjah

The third largest of the seven emirates after Dubai and Abu Dhabi, Sharjah represents 48% of the UAE industrial sector. Special industrial zones span more than 40 sq km, divided into sector-wise subdivisions. Primary industries include oil and gas, industrial plant sale and hire, chemicals, plastics, fiberglass, pipe and a number of other industrial areas.

Sharjah also provides some major incentives to industrial firms. According to official sources, the cost of industrial investment is 35% less than other emirates, as the government pays around 70% of industrial water and electricity costs.

While Sharjah's commercial property areas are not as well-established as either Abu Dhabi and Dubai, there is some considerable investment into this. One notable business area is the Al Khan district with its landmark Petrofac Towers. Sharjah's two free trade zones are Sharjah Airport Free Zone and Hamriyah Free Zone.

Ras Al Khaimah

The fourth largest emirate, 'RAK' is far more rural than its three larger neighbours. At the same time, through its three cement

RAK Business Park

manufacturing plants, it is the UAE's largest cement producer, a major export of the country. It is also home to the world's largest manufacturer of ceramic porcelain tiles, RAK Ceramics, which has annual global sales of US$1 billion. Another major industry is pharmaceuticals; RAK-based Gulf Pharmaceutical Industries distributes to more than 45 countries.

Other industries include quarrying, natural gas processing, and cargo handling through Saqr Port. Ras Al Khaimah's three free trade zones are RAK Investment Authority (RAKIA), RAK Free Zone and RAK Maritime City.

Fujairah

Positioned on the east coast of the UAE, it would be difficult to get more of a contrast between the UAE's larger emirates and the sleepy town of Fujairah, the UAE's fifth-largest emirate. Nestled between a relatively unspoilt sandy coastline and the dramatic jagged landscape of the Hajar Mountain range that runs through from Oman, Fujairah is as much as anything else a short getaway retreat from the stresses and strains of living in the larger emirates. For its size, it also receives a more-than fair volume of international visitors.

While tourism remains a large proportion of its business, Fujairah still has its share of industries in areas such as cement manufacture, plastics, perfumes and textiles. But possibly its biggest area of industry is Port of Fujairah, which has the world's second-largest oil bunkering facility after Singapore. Fujairah's own free zones comprise Fujairah Free Zone and Fujairah Creative City.

Umm Al Quwain

Neighbouring Ras Al Khaimah, Umm Al Quwain is the UAE's sixth-largest emirate and enjoys a similar rural feel. Like many of the smaller emirates, Umm Al Quwain's industry base revolves largely around manufacturing in cement, plastics, aluminium, fiberglass, and other such industries. Its free zone, Ahmed Bin Rashid Free Zone, has a quay wall to receive ocean-going vessels, with 118,000m^2 reserved for light industrial development.

Ajman

The smallest of the seven emirates is Ajman, which borders Sharjah. In addition to its port activities, the tiny emirate's main economic sectors are real estate, financial services and manufacturing (including tobacco, rubber, plastics, chemicals and textiles). It has one free zone, Ajman Free Zone Authority.

RAS AL KHAIMAH HAS THE WORLD'S LARGEST MANUFACTURER OF CERAMIC PORCELAIN TILES, RAK CERAMICS, WHICH HAS ANNUAL GLOBAL SALES OF US$1 BILLION

UAE LAW

Aside from the plethora of laws and regulations you'll encounter when setting up a business, there are also rules specific to the UAE that you should consider once you're up and running. Some of these are general laws, while others come under the companies law.

The UAE's Commercial Companies Law (CCL) is currently being revised and the new additions are likely to be approved by the president very soon. These new laws should help to stimulate the economy further while also attracting further foreign investment, although it is expected to stop short of the initial proposals that would allow 100% foreign ownership of companies in the UAE outside of free zones.

What is expected are measures to make limited liability companies and joint stock companies easier to manage, which would be more attractive to investors, especially the expected reduction from 55% to 30% of the minimum free float in initial public offers. This would mean companies can float on the stock exchange, but directors can still maintain a majority as is the case in many other leading stock exchanges, such as London.

More stringent regulation in areas such as companies making loans to their directors is likely to be joined by a law that will make a company's documentation publicly available, helping to unveil some of the shrouds that may be perceived to be in place in UAE business. Ultimately, these measures should help bring the UAE in line with many of the most established markets around the world, making for a less daunting environment for foreign investors.

One law that has already been approved, although only of benefit to Emiratis, is the SMEs law. It means that small and medium Emirati-owned businesses must be used for 10% of federal authorities and ministries' procurement budgets, and 5% of the budgets of companies with a federal government stake of over 25%. The law also exempts relevant SMEs from customs tax on raw materials, equipment and goods for production purposes, and exempts them from bank guarantees they currently have to pay per new worker.

While this law doesn't affect expats or foreign companies, it highlights the UAE government's continuing desire to promote small business, and could possibly set a precedent for future laws that will be applicable to all.

The following are some of the key legal areas that business owners should be aware of once they've followed the full set-up procedure. For regulations concerning employment, see UAE Labour Laws later on in this guide.

Debt

The UAE's laws are not particularly sophisticated when it comes to debt. Debt, whether in business or a personal debt, is dealt with under the same criminal law that rape or murder might be. In other words, if you default on payment (or bounce a cheque) then there's a strong chance you could end up in prison. Some companies like this as it effectively means they can use the police as debt collectors. However, like any law, people risk 'getting away with it', as was the case with many expats who fled the UAE and their debts in the wake of the financial crisis in 2009.

While reforms are underway, in the meantime it is wise to carry out due diligence with any company you are using. If using a supplier, or supplying another company, it's prudent to have a contract written that contains a clause stating that disputes go through private arbitration, rather than going through courts. This is both a cheaper and faster way to get a resolution.

Free Zone Law

Several Free Trade Zones have their own courts to handle arbitration, such as Dubai International Financial Centre. Here, the DIFC Judicial Authority is an independent, common law judicial system overseeing civil and commercial disputes pertaining to companies within DIFC.

Bankruptcy

Similarly to the issue of debt, the UAE doesn't currently have measures in place that can help companies facing bankruptcy. For start-ups, particularly those with a fair element of risk attached to them, this can be off-putting enough to resist starting a company at all. This is particularly worrying when you consider the UAE's rankings in the World Bank's International Finance Corporation's annual report, which put it 128th in protecting investors, 101st in resolving insolvency and 104th in enforcing contracts. While the country ranks highly in the world for starting a business, the performance at the other end of the scale is certainly cause for concern.

With the realisation that having a structured process to help those business that fall into trouble, and also their creditors, a draft for a new law has already been published. Until then, bankruptcy is likely to land you in significant legal trouble.

Company Closure

If you find you need to close your company, there are certain processes you must go about doing; specifically you should satisfy the de-registration requirements set by the UAE government authorities.

Initially, an application to de-register your company should be made to the Ministry of Economy (MOE), which includes the submission of original licences. The MOE will then make a public announcement on your willingness to close the business, which will notify creditors of your intentions and the fact you're going to liquidate the company's assets. This gives 30 days' notice to any third party that you may owe money or products to. It's then imperative to meet any contractual obligations and liabilities towards those third parties, which is overseen by the Department of Economy. This includes fulfilling obligations to staff, which includes paying outstanding holiday pay and gratuity payments.

Without doing this, the authorities will not de-register a foreign company and the bank guarantee you initially paid is in danger of being forfeited. You'll also find you will be blacklisted and may not be able to leave or re-enter the UAE, and you may face civil and even criminal charges. Once you've satisfied the authorities, you'll also have to pay de-registration and cancellation fees.

Shariah Law

Shariah is the basis of all legal systems on the UAE, both criminal and civil. However, the direct influence of Shariah in the UAE is largely confined to social laws such as child custody and divorce, and most commercial and financial matters are dealt with by the UAE's civil courts (see later). Generally, non-Muslims are not required to appear before a Shariah court, but this does not mean that expat entrepreneurs in the UAE are completely unaffected by Islamic legal frameworks.

Several core principles of Shariah have influenced business transactions and business laws in the UAE. Therefore, anyone managing a business needs to be aware of the following:

· You cannot make money from interest (Riba)

· Risk should be shared, and investors should share in profit and loss in proportion to the amount they invested

· There should be no uncertainty in a contract and both parties must agree all terms of the contract in advance (Gharar)

· Shariah forbids earning money by investing in unethical businesses such as those that involve alcohol, pork, pornography, gambling or other things forbidden to Muslims, so you will find that all Islamic banks and investment firms invest only in ethically acceptable business ventures

SEVERAL CORE PRINCIPLES OF SHARIAH LAW HAVE INFLUENCED BUSINESS TRANSACTIONS AND BUSINESS LAWS IN THE UAE

TOP TIPS FOR
SETTING UP A BUSINESS

1. **Check the available free zone offices and preconditions**
    Often the published information for a free zone showcases a wide choice of offices, but in reality the availability is limited. It's possible that when you go to register the company you may find that only certain office sizes are available. It may be too late to change your free zone by then, so do not proceed with your application until all office features have been confirmed.

2. **Check, check and check again**
    Before you finalise your start-up plan, it is wise to confirm the validity of the published information. At both free zone authorities and local Departments of Economic Development, rules are prone to change.

3. **Choose a flexible model**
    Do not choose a licence category without confirming it can support your business model. A UAE start-up is likely to need flexibility when operating in such a fast-growth landscape, so ensure that you choose a model that allows for future tweaks where necessary. Do not choose a licence category that is too narrow.

4. **Do not open a bank account without confirming the bank charges**
    Banks levy varying charges. For a business start-up based in the UAE, these can amount to a substantial sum for a bank-dependent operation. Always confirm the requirements and charges beforehand.

5. **Do not sign a sponsorship with a local sponsor without a written legal agreement**
    A UAE-based start-up may need a lot of support initially. A local sponsor may want to charge separately for some services. Do not go ahead with sponsorship until both sides have agreed on what to expect from each other and a written agreement is drawn up. Do not rely only on verbal understanding.

REGULATION UPDATES

Make sure you check any updates to laws before you take the plunge, as the UAE continues to speed ahead in its mission for a diversified economy, often changing regulations to ease the process.

Source: Varal LLC

FINANCE AND LOANS

It's not unusual for small and medium enterprises (SMEs) to require some additional financial help, either at the start-up phase or when looking to expand. Fortunately, the United Arab Emirates' large number of local and international banks are well set up to offer assistance, although you need to make sure your business plan is solid and well thought through as rejection rates hover at around 50%.

This is down to the fact that since the financial crisis, UAE banks must conduct more intensive risk analyses of SME business plans. They're also more keen to lend to businesses in free zones as the business costs there are lower, therefore the likelihood of a business being able to pay them back is theoretically higher.

That said, the desire of the UAE government to diversify the economy through entrepreneurial start-ups is likely to lead to increasing options from both banks and alternative funding sources over the coming years.

Business Loans

Most banks now have a dedicated department to facilitate business loan applications. Typically these don't require collateral and repayments are over a period of no more than 48 months. Terms vary, but often the bank will expect your business to have been trading for at least two years and may require a relatively high annual turnover of at least Dhs.3 million. Shop around though, as banks like RAKBANK and National Bank of Fujairah (NBF) have introduced collateral-free business loans with added incentives such as longer repayment terms.

Asset-based Lending

If your company's overall credit is not great but it owns good quality assets, then loans can be secured against those assets. The lending bank will assess the value and then loans against the asset collateral value accordingly. Obviously, struggle to pay back the loan and you could risk losing the very tools or premises you need to carry on in business. However, the higher risk on your part often means the greater likelihood of being accepted for a loan by the bank.

Company Credit Cards

Company, or corporate, credit cards are available from virtually all UAE banks. Most of the time these offer additional benefits such as executive lounge access at airports or travel insurance (similar to benefits offered on personal credit cards) and have itemised billing at the end of the month to make keeping on top of expenses and accounts easier. Some corporate credit cards require a significant deposit, equal to the credit card limit. You still have to pay the card off every month and only when you cancel the credit card do you get the security deposit back.

Working Capital Options

There is a number of short term finance options to consider in order to keep the cashflow flowing.

Overdrafts

Overdrafts on business current accounts are available and can be a useful tool to keep your business flowing. Interest is generally charged at a daily rate.

Letter of Credit

A supplier may ask you for an irrevocable letter of credit in their favour to secure a trade finance transaction. That means the bank issues them a letter of credit on your behalf and a commitment to the supplier that the bank will pay them if they keep their side of the transaction. Effectively, this puts the supplier's trust in the bank, rather than in you, which can be useful when starting up. This can be set up on a revolving basis too, effectively helping to keep your business operations flowing smoothly.

Factoring

If you have confirmed sales orders or accounts receivables, then a number of banks will now loan you finance on the back of these. This may be an essential injection of cash that will help you to fulfil those orders and allow you to continue with growing.

Invoice Financing

If you need to keep your cash flow flowing and can't wait for unpaid invoices to be honoured, then it's possible for some banks to pay you immediate cash advances of up to 90% of the invoiced amount.

Alternative Funding

It's worth considering that there is also a number of public funds set up for establishing SMEs, such as the Khalifa Fund in Abu Dhabi or the Mohammed Bin Rashid Fund in Dubai. If banks or public funds can't help, then there's always the option of approaching a private equity or venture capital firm, of which there are a number in the UAE, each of which specialise in specific business areas.

For example, twofour54 in Abu Dhabi (see Free Zones) can offer financial backing to creative industries, or N2V (n2v.com), which has an office in Dubai, looks to invest in e-commerce and mobile technology. Some free zones offer financing programmes to companies set up within that zone, such as TECOM or Silicon Oasis, both in Dubai.

THE DESIRE OF THE UAE GOVERNMENT TO DIVERSIFY THE ECONOMY THROUGH ENTREPRENEURIAL START-UPS IS LIKELY TO LEAD TO INCREASING OPTIONS FROM BOTH BANKS AND ALTERNATIVE FUNDING SOURCES OVER THE COMING YEARS

Failing all of that, there's the very modern idea of crowdfunding. If your business idea requires only a relatively small amount of financing then online sites allow you to raise money from a large number of investors in exchange for equity, or for special rewards should your company succeed. Popular sites include crowdfunder.com, kickstarter.com and indiegogo.com.

UAE Financial Advisors

Acuma 04 332 8582, *acuma.ae*
AES International 04 450 2500, *aesinternational.com*
Armanie Advisors 04 388 8576, *amanieadvisors.com*
Continental Financial Services 04 509 1555, *continental-intl.com*
Globaleye 800 4558, *globaleye.com*
Holborn Assets 04 457 3800, *holbornassets.com*
Intra Group 04 220 6899, *intradebt.ae*
PIC Middle East 02 509 0500, *pic-uae.com*
Synergy Financial 04 321 6694, *synergyfinancial.ae*
The ONE Group 800 663 663, *theonegroup.co*

UAE & Offshore Banks

Abu Dhabi Commercial Bank 800 2030, *adcb.com*
Abu Dhabi Islamic Bank 800 2288, *adib.ae*
Al Ahli Bank of Kuwait 04 607 5555, *abk.eahli.com*

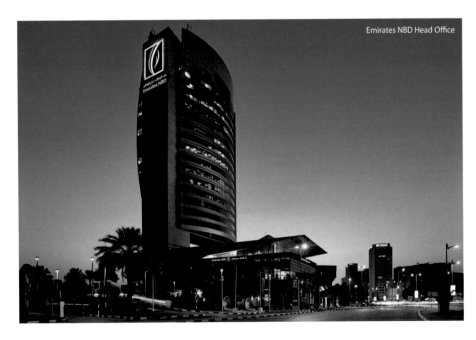
Emirates NBD Head Office

Al Khaliji Bank 04 222 2291, *alkhaliji.ae*
ANZ 04 359 1500, *anz.com*
Arab African International Bank 04 393 7773, *aaibank.com*
Bank Melli Iran 04 201 5100, *bmi.ae*
Bank of Baroda 800 BARODA, *bankofbarodauae.ae*
Bank of New York Mellon 04 425 2524, *bnymellonam.com*
Bank Sarasin – Alpen 04 363 4300, *sarasin-alpen.com*
Banque De Commerce Et De Placements 04 425 0800, *bcp-bank.com*
Barclays 800 428 6080, *barclays.ae*
Citibank 04 311 4000, *citibank.com/uae*
Credit Agricole Corporate & Investment Bank 04 376 1100, *ca-cib.com*
Deutsche Bank 04 319 9523, *db.com*
Doha Bank 04 343 9111, *dohabank.ae*
Emirates NBD 600 540 000, *emiratesnbd.com*
Habib Bank AG Zurich 04 422 2400, *habibbank.com*
HSBC Bank Middle East 600 55H SBC, *hsbc.ae*
Korea Exchange Bank 04 228 1133, *keb.co.kr*
National Bank of Abu Dhabi 800 2211, *nbad.com*
National Bank of Fujairah 800 8NBF, *nbf.ae*
RAK Bank Head Office 07 206 2222, *rakbankdirect.ae*
Royal Bank of Canada 04 331 3196, *rbcwminternational.com*
The Royal Bank of Scotland 04 506 2101, *rbsbank.ae*
Societe Generale Private Banking 04 425 7600, *privatebanking.societegenerale.ae*
Standard Chartered Bank 600 522 288, *sc.com*
UBS 04 210 8500, *ubs.com*

UAE Accountants

Alliott Hadi Shahid Chartered Accountants 04 222 7355, *alliottuae.com*
Crowe Horwath 04 447 3951, *crowehorwath.net*
Deloitte 04 376 8888, *deloitte.com*
Griffin Nagda & Company 04 297 5010, *griffinnagda.com*
Kant & Clients 04 221 2168, *kantandclients.com*
Kothari 04 352 6330, *kothariauditors.com*
Mashal Al Zarooni Chartered Accountants 04 358 9996, *mazca.ae*
MBK Auditing 04 250 7768, *mbkauditing.com*
Morison Menon Chartered Accountants 04 887 1727, *morisonmenon.com*
Paul & Hassan 04 337 9966, *paulhassan.com*
PKF UAE 04 388 8900, *pkfuae.com*
Saif Chartered Accountants 04 451 8600, *saifaudit.com*
Talal Abu-Ghazaleh International 04 396 7778, *tagi.com*
Tamim Chartered Accountants 04 396 2980, *tamimaudit.com*

IT'S WORTH CONSIDERING THAT THERE IS ALSO A NUMBER OF PUBLIC FUNDS SET UP FOR ESTABLISHING SMES, SUCH AS THE KHALIFA FUND IN ABU DHABI OR THE MOHAMMED BIN RASHID FUND IN DUBAI

COMMERCIAL PROPERTY

For any company starting up in the UAE or elsewhere, an essential step is establishing a premises from which to conduct your business. For a step-by-step guide to leasing commercial property, see How To... No.6.

The UAE provides a diverse range of office districts tailored to different occupier profiles. Dubai provides the largest amount of office space with over seven million sq m spread across the various office areas. Abu Dhabi has around three million sq m. The smaller emirates of Sharjah, Ajman, Fujairah, Umm Al Quwain and Ras Al Khaimah provide office space to service the local markets and the free zones established within them.

Deciding whether to rent or own property is a commercial decision that will depend on your company's requirements. Some companies prefer to own their office. Others prefer to lease and deploy their capital into the activities of the business.

Renting

Apart from company-related registration and licensing fees, there are no taxes payable on renting a property. Within some areas, however, a community fee is payable based on the office area occupied. This is directly payable to either the master developer or community manager.

Leasing Facilities

For larger operations, leasing an industrial or office facility will be your preferred route. In the UAE, property is leased in four different ways; gross lease, triple-net-lease, land lease and modified net lease. Leases generally cover longer periods (up to 99 years), compared to rents which can be weekly, monthly or annually.

Commonly, a modified net lease is the most popular option, as it means a shared responsibility between tenant and landlord for property related charges such as taxes, maintenance and insurance. Triple-net-leases put the majority of these costs on the tenant. A gross lease, if you can find one, is often a higher fixed price for the tenant but the landlord covers the extra charges. Typically, most industrial, retail and multi-tenant properties are leased under modified net lease agreements.

Alternatively, if your ambitions are high and you need to construct your own premises, then a longer-term land lease allows you to do just that. You pay for the construction and rent the land, then at the end of the lease the landlord gets the land back along with any building on it.

The Burj Khalifa and Downtown Dubai

Retail

For retail businesses, malls are arguably one of the first areas to look at due to the high concentration of keen shoppers they attract. In Dubai, supply of units is currently struggling to keep up with demand for retail space. The city's well-established international reputation as a shopping destination creates huge demand from retailers. Occupancy in the main malls is upward of 98% with substantial waiting lists, so get your name on the list sooner rather than later. Also, be prepared to pay a premium as rental prices remain high at around US$114 per square metre.

Abu Dhabi shows a different picture. With the huge Yas Mall opening in time for the 2014 Formula 1 Grand Prix, supply is currently outstripping demand with the opening of a number of large malls. This keeps prices lower, at around US$71 per square metre, which can make it an attractive proposition when factoring in the city's emerging tourist destination status.

Starting smaller, the outside stalls at markets in both Dubai and Abu Dhabi can be a good entry point. Comparatively low lease rates make them an ideal testing ground for your products, although stipulations generally state products should be locally-sourced items such as organic fruit and veg, home decor or gifts.

Buying

Within Dubai and Abu Dhabi there are specific areas where non-GCC nationals and companies can purchase commercial property. In Dubai these areas are referred to as freehold areas and include:

- Business Bay
- Downtown Dubai
- Dubai International Financial Centre (DIFC)
- Dubai Investment Park (allowing up to an 85-year ground lease)
- Dubai Silicon Oasis
- Dubailand
- Jumeirah Lakes Towers (JLT)
- Marsa Dubai (Dubai Marina)
- TECOM (a master developer of many of Dubai's business parks)

Jebel Ali Free Zone has plots available on long-term leases for companies to develop their own warehousing, office and industrial facilities.

Abu Dhabi currently has two investment areas that have commercial space available to purchase within:

- Al Maryah Island (the location for the Abu Dhabi World Financial Free Zone, similar to Dubai's DIFC district)
- Al Reem Island

Real Estate Agents

Al Baraha Land Real Estate 04 272 2999, *albaraharealestate.com*
Al Batha Real Estate 06 574 7477, *bathaestate.com*
Al Fajer Properties 04 454 2633, *alfajerproperties.com*
Al Futtaim Real Estate 04 213 6497, *afrealestate.com*
Al Ghurair Real Estate 04 262 3377, *alghurair.com*
Al Hathboor Real Estate 04 282 8289, *alhathboorrealestate.com*
Allsopp & Allsopp 04 323 7720, *allsoppandallsopp.com*
Al Mazaya Real Estate 800 101 01, *mazayarealestate.com*
Al Odaid Real Estate 800 632 43, *alodaid.ae*
Always Property 04 452 2267, *always-property.com*
Better Homes 600 522 212, *bhomes.com*
FAM Properties 04 447 3573, *famproperties.com*
Knight Frank 04 451 2000
MENA Properties 04 388 9963, *mena-properties.com*
Provident Estate 800 ESTATE, *providentestate.com*
Sweet Homes Real Estate 800 794 6637, *sweethomesuae.com*

CREDIT: *This section has been written with the professional advice of Simon Whittle, property consultant with Colliers International.*

RENTAL PRICES

Colliers International provides some indicative prices on renting in key commercial property areas within Abu Dhabi, Dubai and the northern emirates

Average rent per square foot (Dhs). Rental pricing is based on average office rents in Q2 2014.

DUBAI

Free Zone Areas	Grade A	Grade B	Trend
Internet City & Media City	200	180	↗
DIFC	240	180	↗
Dubai Silicon Oasis (DSO)	80	60	⇄
Dubai World Central (DWC)	105	N/A	↗
Jebel Ali Free Zone (JAFZA)	180	180	↗
Jumeriah Lakes Towers (JLT)	120	90	↗

Mainland Areas	Grade A	Grade B	Trend
Bur Dubai/Oud Metha	110	90	⇄
Business Bay	140	90	↗
Deira	110	90	⇄
Downtown Dubai	180	120	↗
Dubai Investment Park	70	60	↗
Sheikh Zayed Road	160	120	⇄
Al Barsha	120	90	↗

ABU DHABI

Free Zone Areas	Grade A	Grade B	Trend
Al Maryah Island	200	N/A	↗
Abu Dhabi Airport Free Zone	165	N/A	↗
Masdar City	170	N/A	↗

Mainland Areas	Grade A	Grade B	Trend
Al Khalidiya	160	110	↗
Al Nahyan	140	100	⇄
Al Reem Island	140	120	↗
Capital Centre	185	135	↗
Corniche	180	140	↗
Hamdan Street	140	110	⇄
Khalifa Park	140	120	↗
Mushrif / Danet	150	110	⇄
Tourist Club	135	110	⇄

NORTHERN EMIRATES

Free Zone Areas	Grade A	Grade B	Trend
Sharjah Airport Free Zone (SAIF)	155	N/A	↗
Ras Al Khaimah Free Trade Zone	90	N/A	↗

Colliers International publishes regular market reports on colliers.com

RENTAL PRICES

At the time of going to print, average rental prices in Dubai vary greatly. In the free zones, rents range from Dhs.60 per square foot in Dubai Silicon Oasis to Dhs.180 in Dubai Internet City. In popular mainland areas, rents range from Dhs.90 per square foot in Business Bay, to Dhs.120 in Downtown Dubai.

THE INS AND OUTS OF FINDING COMMERCIAL PROPERTY

Simon Whittle, property consultant with global real estate firm, Colliers International, provides his insights into the main areas to set up, how tos, market trends and price indications within the UAE commercial property market.

Simon Whittle
Business Colliers International
Web colliers.com
Activities Real estate

How is the market currently performing?
Overall, the UAE property sector has recovered from the economic downturn with higher occupancy and expansion of companies. This has limited supply in some areas. Regional free zone business hubs such as Dubai Internet City, Dubai Media City and Jebel Ali now have more than 95% occupancy, with new supply underway to provide additional space.

Onshore office spaces, particularly in freehold areas, have experienced a large volume of supply in recent years. That said, steady absorption is beginning to reduce the vacancy rate, with good quality single-owned buildings experiencing vacancy rates of less than 20% and jointly owned properties 30% or less.

Buildings that are well-maintained, provide efficient floor plates and good management experience the highest demands, with sought-after buildings experiencing very high occupancy rates. Older buildings that have not upgraded their facilities and provide less-efficient floor plates are experiencing higher vacancy, with tenants moving to more modern, cost effective buildings.

Lease Registration

Commercial tenancy contracts must be registered with the relevant municipality, such as Dubai Land Department's Ejari and Abu Dhabi's Tawtheeq online systems.

Renting: important considerations
Within the UAE, it is common for an incoming tenant to pay the landlord's agent or real estate company a leasing fee of 5% of the first year's rent. Some landlords do not charge this fee, but as a general rule it is expected that the tenant pays it. This applies across all property types.

Lease terms ranging from one to five years are common, and longer leases of 10 years have become more common for larger occupiers. Rent-free periods are provided for a tenant to undertake its fit-out.

A tenant can lease in all office locations within the UAE, but is restricted by the company licence obtained: a free zone company can only operate from within the applicable free zone and an onshore company can only operate from an onshore building.

Buying: important considerations
Land transfer fees payable are currently 4% in Dubai and 2% in Abu Dhabi. Within Dubai, this is split between buyer and seller. However, this is for both parties to negotiate, and generally in a rising market the buyer pays this fee. Real estate broker fees are 2% of the net purchase price and generally payable by the seller. For some off-plan properties no broker fees are payable, while the developer pays brokers a referral fee.

For 'strata' properties (where there are multiple owners within a single building) service charges are set by an owners' association and payable for the maintenance, repair and upkeep of the building. These are often based pro-rata on the area occupied. Each emirate has different regulations for the establishment of owners associations and the enforcement of fees payable.

What factors determine price?
Within all office markets there are different grades of property that appeal to various occupier profiles. Office rents and sale prices are reflected in the building location, quality, floor plate efficiency (greater use of open plan office space) and demand.

Office rental rates in prime commercial districts are internationally competitive with many comparable buildings, providing more affordable accommodation than other regional hubs such as London, Hong Kong and Singapore.

What else is there to consider?
Operational expenses are sometimes excluded within the rental price. Be sure to check whether the following is included:

- Air conditioning supply
- Service charges for common areas: some landlords apply either a fixed percentage of the rent or a flat rate per square foot
- Car parking: how many spaces, and is there additional parking available to lease
- Fit-out costs: many newer office buildings are handed over in a shell and core condition, meaning raised floors, ceiling, air conditioning and lighting need to be installed

ONSHORE OFFICE SPACES, PARTICULARLY IN FREEHOLD AREAS, HAVE EXPERIENCED A LARGE VOLUME OF SUPPLY IN RECENT YEARS

MAINLAND
BUSINESS

CHOOSING MAINLAND MEANS FREEDOM TO TRADE ANYWHERE IN THE UAE, FEWER RESTRICTIONS ON CHOICE OF LOCATION AND NO CORPORATION TAXES

A BUSINESS CAN HAVE

10

ACTIVITIES PER
TRADE LICENCE

SOME
BUSINESS
ACTIVITIES
REQUIRE
SPECIAL
APPROVAL

Any company set up in the United Arab Emirates that is not in a Free Trade Zone (free zone) is considered to be a mainland business. This business will be directly registered under that emirate's government.

Under UAE law, any mainland business must be wholly owned by UAE nationals; if it is a foreign company, it must have a UAE national as a sponsor with a 51% share of the business, or have sponsorship from a local service agent. If you are setting up a professional company, you can own 100% of the company but the sponsorship of a local service agent is still a requirement.

Why Mainland?

While it can be a tricky procedure to set up, the advantages of being a mainland business are that you're free to trade anywhere in the UAE, and you face fewer restrictions on where you can locate your office or retail outlet, and on getting employment visas. There are also no corporation taxes to pay.

Advantages

The main advantages of establishing a mainland business are:

- You're free to trade in any part of the UAE
- No restrictions on registration, visas and legal requirements
- No restrictions on recruitment
- No yearly auditing
- No corporate tax
- Flexibility to rent office anywhere
- No limitations in getting employment visas

The following pages document the procedures involved in establishing a mainland business (some are also relevant to free zones).

Trade Licence

Licences are valid for one year, but any business can request a licence for up to four years with the Department of Economic Development's permission. There are three types of trade licence available to a mainland business:

- **Commercial Licences:** all kinds of trading activity
- **Professional Licences:** professions, services, craftsmen and artisans
- **Industrial Licences**: industrial or manufacturing activities

As part of a trade licence application, you will need to select your business activity, and your legal form (see Your Options).

Selecting A Business Activity

A business can have a maximum of 10 activities per trade licence. Contact the DED for a full list of business activities, which fall into

Trade licenses are required

different groups. If your business activity is not listed, you will need to email the DED with a description of the activity. The DED may then create a new business activity for you, with a required code for the trade licence application. Some activities require a special approval from government bodies other than the DED.

How to apply for a trade licence

1) Apply for residence visa (see Working in the UAE)
2) Register your trade name
3) Appoint a UAE national sponsor or local service agent
4) Apply for an Initial Approval Certificate
5) Obtain special licensing approvals (if required)
6) Rent/buy commercial premises
7) Apply for a full trade licence

Once you have a trade licence you will then need to:

8) Register with the Chamber of Commerce & Industry for that emirate (some small businesses and artisans are exempt)
9) Obtain a company PO Box

Then, to recruit staff, you will need to appoint a commercial agent, and apply for a PRO card, establishment labour card, establishment immigration card, and immigration and individual labour cards. See How Tos... Nos.14-17.

THE ADVANTAGES OF BEING A MAINLAND BUSINESS ARE THAT YOU'RE FREE TO TRADE ANYWHERE IN THE UAE, AND YOU FACE FEWER RESTRICTIONS

HELPING SME'S
DHLIVER

ON TIME, EVERY TIME

When it comes to growing your business, delivery expertise is everything.
That is why you can rely on us as your trusted partner to ensure your deliveries
are where they need to be, on time, every time.

Open an account today to **SAVE 50%***
and see how we can deliver growth for your business.

Call one of our International Specialists on 042924330
or log on www.dhl.ae

EXCELLENCE. SIMPLY DELIVERED.

"YOU NEED TWO THINGS: A GOOD PRO SERVICE AND ACCESS TO CAPITAL"

Dina Ghandour

Business yApparel
Web yApparel.com
Activities Retail – yoga clothing store
Strengths PR / Marketing / Communications

With a background in PR and communications, Dina Ghandour decided to create yApparel after recognising there were limited options for best-in-class yoga and fitness apparel in the UAE. The store's physical and web presence serves as a focal point for the booming local yoga and Pilates communities.

What made you decide to set up your business in the UAE?
The UAE's steady economy, high footfall of tourists, and diverse population make it a fertile ground for entrepreneurs to see their dreams come to fruition.

How did you decide which type of trade licence to get and whether to set up in a free zone or mainland?
As a retailer, I could take either of two paths when it comes to obtaining a trade licence in Dubai: specialist equipment trading, or a general trading licence. I wanted to leave room for both lateral and vertical growth in my business, and decided to go head on with a licence that allows me to both import and export a variety of goods. There are pros and cons for setting up in both mainland or freezone – it really depends on the nature of your business. While a free zone would have allowed me 100% ownership over my business, and potentially cheaper rent, I would be limited by location and additional fees. As a retail outlet, it was important to set up in Dubai mainland.

Any Advice?

Female entrepreneurs will surely experience some prejudice – as there seems to be a sense that women are not as switched on into business, and technology, or construction, or financials. If possible, get your big brother, male cousin or father involved.

How long did it take to turn your idea into reality?
It took almost 10 months from when I got the idea, until our doors opened in March 2014. Opening a business in the UAE, while extremely feasible, can also prove to be a struggle in some areas – such as finding an affordable space amidst skyrocketing rents, working with contractors who fail to deliver on time, to waiting months to obtain specific certificates from the regulatory bodies.

What is your biggest motivation as a woman in business?
It's already a challenge to set up any business alone, and in some parts of the world it can be even more challenging as a woman.

But, ultimately, it's about being a business starter, not just a woman in business.

What resources did you use during the process of setting up?
I used a fantastic PRO service, One Stop Business Centre. Otherwise, I feel formal organisations and support groups for non-Emirati entrepreneurs are quite limited in the UAE.

What was your biggest obstacle in setting up in the UAE?
The contractors who were in charge of fitting our space out. The other thing to look out for are all the various (and seemingly arbitrary) fees associated with various processes that you will never think to budget for.

How do you switch off from the constant pressure?
It doesn't really ever 'switch off' – not at the beginning at least. It takes a lot of self-discipline to make sure you are allowing space to step away, do your hobbies, see family – which is very important to ensuring you keep your sanity and inspiration flowing.

Do you feel it has all been worth it?
Absolutely! It's a once in a lifetime experience, and is something to learn from whether we succeed or fail.

THE UAE'S STEADY ECONOMY, HIGH FOOTFALL OF TOURISTS, AND DIVERSE POPULATION MAKE IT A FERTILE GROUND FOR ENTREPRENEURS TO SEE THEIR DREAMS COME TO FRUITION

2

HOW TO...

REGISTER A TRADE NAME

When applying for a trade licence, you will need to register your company's trade name and have it approved by the Department of Economic Development (DED). The DED can reject a trade name if it doesn't comply with the prerequisites.

You can apply online in most emirates if you have a Business Registration & Licensing (BRL) account, or go through an authorised service centre or law firm.

PREREQUISITES
Your trade name:
• Must not use the word Abu Dhabi, Ajman, Dubai, Fujairah, Ras Al Khaimah, Sharjah, or Umm al Quwain
• Must not conflict with Arabic and Islamic traditions
• Must not refer to God or Islam
• Should be translated into Arabic
• Should be indicative of the business activity

BUSINESS REGISTRATION AND LICENSING

If you are setting up in Dubai, sign up for a Business Registration and Licensing (BRL) online account (set up by Dubai's Department of Economic Development) to access all trade licensing services, pay fees online, and book appointments with DED staff. Register at dubaided.gov.ae; verification requires a visit to any DED office. An increasing number of BRL services are also accessible on the Business in Dubai smart app: you can get licences issued or renewed, reserve or renew trade names, get initial approvals, check status of licences and their legal forms, and pay fines.

WHAT TO BRING
• Trade name application form is available at DED offices or online at the DED website
• Fees: the cost for obtaining a trade name varies depending on the content and language (approximately Dhs.1,000)

PROCEDURE
WHERE: Department of Economic Development (DED)
• Search at eservices.dubaided.gov.ae/ to check that trade name does not already exist
• Submit form to the DED, often at the same time as you apply for a trade licence
• A Trade Name Certificate is valid for 60 days
• It can be renewed online only once
• It must be renewed within one week before it is due to expire

RESTRICTIONS
Trade names that cannot be reserved include: name of country, name of continent, famous regions and towns, colours. Foreign words and short words will be charged at an extra fee of Dhs. 2,000 per year.

For an annual fee of Dhs.1,000 the following trade names may be given to local companies:
• A name indicating the company's market. (e.g. 'National', 'Gulf', 'International', 'Global', 'Asian', or 'Regional')
• A word within a name indicating the company's activity
• A foreign name for a company (including the trade name or trademark of an international company) can only be used with the owner's written approval
For an annual fee of Dhs. 2,000, the following trade names may be given to local companies:
• Foreign name for an ordinary company can be used only if, the Arabic word can be pronounced in English as well
• A company name can be written as an abbreviation only if it has the same lettering in both Arabic or English
• The company name includes the words 'UAE', 'Emirates', 'Dubai' and 'Gulf'
• A name that includes numbers

DEPARTMENT OF ECONOMIC DEVELOPMENT

The DED acts as a one-stop shop and coordinates with other ministries in terms of additional required approvals. To simplify procedures, the DED has launched various e-services including trade name reservation, licence renewal and initial registration.

Trade names

3A

HOW TO...

APPOINT A SPONSOR

By law, foreign nationals setting up a company outside of a free zone must sign a Local Agency Agreement with a UAE national. The local agent is referred to as a 'sponsor'. The sponsor (not to be confused with the terms 'commercial agent' or 'local service agent') is obliged to assist with all government-related issues, such as obtaining permits, trade licences, visas and labour cards.

The sponsor's signature will be required for most application forms. In return, they own 51% of the company and will receive a percentage of the profits. If you do not have a sponsor, you can contact the Advocates Law Firm (theadvocates.ae) which has a recommended list.

PREREQUISITES
• Sponsor must either be a UAE national or a company that is 100%-owned by UAE nationals
• Setting up an LLC or public/private shareholding company

WHAT TO BRING
• Passport and Resident ID of business owner and sponsor (copies)
• Attested Memorandum of Association (original and copy)
• Attested articles of association (original and copy)
• Passports of all board members or partners (copy)
• Letter from DED to certify sponsor is UAE national

SPONSOR'S SHARE

The sponsor is typically a 51% owner of the business on paper. He/she does not invest any of his/her own funds, and you are often obliged to put 51% of your capital in the sponsor's name. In return, he/she will not partake of the profits of the business, but will take either an annual fixed fee or a percentage of revenues.

PROCEDURE
WHERE: Department of Economic Development (DED)
• A contract (Local Agency Agreement) is signed by both parties and notarised
• Legalise the contract if setting up a branch office
• Get contract authenticated at the UAE embassy and Ministry of Foreign Affairs
• Translate contract into Arabic
• Seal contract with notary public of the UAE courts
• Contract is ready to be submitted in all procedures for setting up a company

3B

HOW TO...

APPOINT A LOCAL SERVICE AGENT

Anyone setting up a sole proprietorship, civil business or a branch office must appoint a local service agent, which is essentially a sponsor.

Unlike a UAE national sponsor required for a limited liability company (LLC), a local service agent is paid a fixed fee only for their services and does not receive any commission or profits from the branch office.

PREREQUISITES
• Local service agent must be a UAE national
OR
• Company owned 100% by UAE nationals

WHAT TO BRING
• Passport and Resident ID of business owner and local service agent (copies)

PROCEDURE
WHERE: Department of Economic Development (DED)
• Local Service Agent Agreement is drawn up and authenticated by a notary public
• Contract is signed by both parties
• Agreement is ready

HELPING HAND
Agencies such as Links Group (linksgroup.com), One Stop Dubai (onestopdubai.com) and Quality House (qualityhouse.ae) can assist you in finding a local service agent, as well as providing other set-up business services.

Department of Economic Development

4

HOW TO...

APPLY FOR A TRADE LICENCE (INITIAL APPROVAL)

Once you have selected your business activity and legal form, you can apply for an Initial Approval Certificate from the DED, which gives you the go ahead to start a business and take steps to getting a full trade licence. This certificate records partners, legal type and activities of the trade licence; it is valid for six months and is not renewable. You must register and reserve your trade name before or at the same time as applying for your trade licence.

There are several ways to apply: at a DED branch, through a law firm or PRO registered with the DED, at a government service centre, or online at the DED website.Once you have completed this step, you can lease your business premises and then apply for a full trade licence.

PREREQUISITES
• You are setting up a company outside a free zone
• You have registered your trade name (See Registering a trade name)
• You have sponsorship from a UAE national, who will have a 51% stake in your business (if setting up an LLC or public/ private shareholding company)
OR
• You have sponsorship from a local service agent (if setting up a branch company, sole proprietorship or civil business)

WHAT TO BRING
General
• Trade licence application form (download it at the DED website)
• Proof of reserved trade name
• Approval issued by other government authorities according to the type of activity; call 04 445 5555 to check if this is required
• Company's Memorandum of Association (attested) (two copies)
• Permission from a UAE court to practise business in that emirate (if aged under 21)
• Fee: Dhs.100 for Initial Approval Certificate

Branch company or foreign representative office
• Approval from Ministry of Economy (MOE) for industrial/ commercial licences
• Power of attorney issued in favour of the director for companies not registered with the MOE
• Director's passport (copy)
• Company's board of directors resolution authorising opening of the branch, if not registered with the Ministry of Economy (translated into Arabic)
• Main company's certificate of incorporation (translated into Arabic) (copy)

Individual establishment or sole proprietorship
• Applicant's passport with residence visa (copy)
• NOC from applicant's current sponsor
• Director's passport, if any (copy)

Limited liability company (LLC)
• Applicant's passport with residence visa (copy)
• NOC from applicant's current sponsor
• Director's passport, if any (copy)
• Company's board of directors resolution to subscribe to the new company if the partner is an existing corporate entity in the UAE or abroad (attested and translated into Arabic)

Professional/civil business company
• Applicant's passport with residence visa (copy)
• NOC from applicant's current sponsor

Public or private shareholding company
• Business plan/feasibility study (two copies)

PROCEDURE
WHERE: Department of Economic Development (DED)
• Submit your application with paperwork and fee (plus Dhs.50 fee for copy of licence application) to any DED office
• The initial approval for trade licence is typically granted within one day
• Initial approval is valid for six months, during which time you need to apply for the full trade licence

120 DAYS HASSLE-FREE LICENCE
Dubai's DED has launched a fast-track 120-day licence which enables most business owners to start their business immediately – while completing other registration requirements from other government authorities – within a 120-day grace period. The 120-day option is only available for low or no-risk businesses; businesses categorised as conducting high-risk duties include those dealing with humans, animals and the environment such as restaurants and medical centres.

5

HOW TO...

SPECIAL APPROVAL

Business activities that require special approval include: banks and financial institutions (must apply to the Central Bank of the UAE); insurance companies and related agencies (Ministry of Economy and Commerce); manufacturing companies (Ministry of Finance and Industry); clinics, pharmaceutical and medical products (Ministry of Health).

OBTAIN SPECIAL APPROVAL FOR A BUSINESS ACTIVITY

Certain businesses require additional special approval from various government ministries and/or other authorities, according to their type of activity. You will then need a no objection certificate (NOC) from the ministry related to your business domain before applying for a trade licence.

Some commercial activities are restricted to UAE nationals or companies that are fully owned by UAE nationals; for example, real estate agency and real estate brokerage activities.

PREREQUISITES

- Use the activities search at the DED's website to find out if your business needs special approval – and from which government body/bodies (See Directory for DED websites for each emirate)
- For a list of business activities and related ministries, visit registration and licensing 'external approval' on the DED's websites

WHAT TO BRING

- Completed Initial Approval Form from the DED
- Financial guarantee from a UAE bank (if required)

PROCEDURE

WHERE: Department of Economic Development (DED)
- Take your paperwork and application form to the relevant authorities to request the NOCs
- Submit NOCs with other paperwork required for trade licence to DED
- This process needs to take place once you have submitted your initial trade licence and trade name applications
- Once the business type is approved by the Ministry of Economy, the DED can approve your full trade licence

6

HOW TO...

LEASE A COMMERCIAL PROPERTY

Once you have the Initial Approval Certificate for your trade licence, you can start searching for your ideal physical business address. If you choose to locate your company within an authorised business centre, it's unlikely you will need location-related approvals from the municipality of the emirate.

Below is the process if opening in Dubai, although it's similar in all emirates.

PREREQUISITES
• Initial Approval Certificate

WHAT TO BRING
• Initial Approval Certificate
• Financial guarantee from a local bank (if required)

PROCEDURE
WHERE: Planning Department at Municipality office
• Inform department of selected plot number, size, the landlord's name and your business activity – and get confirmation of its suitability
• Sign your tenancy contract with the landlord and open an account with the electricity and water authority (DEWA in Dubai, ADEWA in Abu Dhabi etc)
• Register your tenancy contract with the relevant emirate Municipality office to protect your rights as a tenant (eg. in Dubai through RERA's online Ejari system; in Abu Dhabi through the online Tawtheeq system)
• Take your municipality-registered tenancy contract, your Initial Approval Form and your Initial Approval Certificate back to the Municipality Planning Department to gain approval on your business location
• If you meet all requirements, the section will stamp the Initial Approval Form

RENT OR BUY?
See the commercial property section earlier on in this chapter for more information on the options for buying or renting commercial property.

7

HOW TO...

APPLY FOR A TRADE LICENCE (FULL)

Once you have completed the steps outlined previously you are ready to apply for the full trade licence.

PREREQUISITES
- Initial Approval Certificate
- Municipality-registered commercial tenancy contract

WHAT TO BRING
General
- Initial Approval Certificate
- Initial Approval Form with stamp from municipality office
- Trade Name Certificate
- Municipality-registered commercial tenancy contract (copy)
- Approvals on your selected business activity from other government departments, if applicable
- MOA or copy of MOA, attested by UAE Ministry of Foreign Affairs, if applicable
- Contract with local service agent OR UAE national sponsor
- Fees: 5% of value of business premises lease agreement; Dhs.1,000-3,000 waste fees; Dhs.480 company registration

Branch company or foreign representative office
- Contract with local service agent notarised by notary public
- If applicable, list of parent company's branches in the UAE
- New branch director's passport and Resident ID (copy)
- Board of directors' resolution from parent company authorising establishment of a branch office in the UAE
- Special approval documents issued by other government authorities (if required)
- Articles and MOA of parent company (copies)
- Power of attorney from parent company authorising branch manager to conduct affairs and sign
- Audited financial statements of the parent company for past two years
- Certificate of corporation stating company form and capital
- Name/s of sponsor, Emirates ID of sponsor for each branch
- Profile of the company trade licence issued and ratified by licensing authority in home country (copy)
- Bank guarantee fee

OPEN FOR BUSINESS
As part of the setting-up process, you will need to submit an application to the DED for a signboard permit to advertise your business trade name in both English and Arabic. This costs around Dhs.1,500. The office premises will also be inspected by the fire and civil defence authorities as well as the DED.

Individual establishment or sole proprietorship
- Contract with local service agent notarised by notary public
- Certificate of capital deposit, issued by one of the specified operating banks

Limited liability company (LLC)
- Local agency agreement with UAE national sponsor
- Company's MOA notarised and translated into Arabic
- Certificate signed by company director
- Certificate from auditors
- Certificate of capital deposit, issued by one of the specified operating banks
- Auditing office licence (copy)

Professional/civil business company
- Contract with local service agent notarised by notary public
- Notarised contract of professional business company

Public or private shareholding company
- Local agency agreement with UAE national sponsor
- Approval from the Ministry of Economy
- List of directors' names, dates and places of birth, occupations and sample of directors' signatures (original and copies)
- Written declaration by each member of board of directors accepting the appointment

PROCEDURE

WHERE: Department of Economic Development (DED)
- Either book an appointment online OR use the walk-in Fanar service at DED offices for an extra fee of Dhs.500
- Submit all documents and fees
- Your trade licence is granted within one to seven days

Branch company procedure
- Must register first with the Ministry of Economy (MOE), then with the DED
- Ministry of Economy will forward application to the Federal Foreign Companies Committee for approval
- Ministry of Economy will then issue the required ministerial licence to the DED, specifying the activity to be practised by the foreign company
- Once received from DED, submit one copy of full trade licence to MOE to have company entered onto Foreign Companies Register

NEXT STEPS
Once you have your trade licence, submit one copy to the Ministry of Economy's Commercial Registration Department, to have the company entered onto the register. You will also need to register with the Chamber of Commerce & Industry.

8

HOW TO...

REGISTER WITH THE CHAMBER OF COMMERCE & INDUSTRY

All commercial and industrial businesses must be registered with the Chamber of Commerce & Industry – unless you are a very small trading outfit or professional. Once your company has been formerly recorded in the Chamber of Commerce register, it is entitled to import and export goods in the UAE.

PREREQUISITES
• Trade licence issued by DED or free zone
• Commercial or industrial premises in the UAE
• Business in operation
• Sound credit rating 10 years prior to application
• No theft, fraud or forgery convictions 10 years prior to application

WHAT TO BRING
• Passport of the partners/attorney (copy)
• Signature card, sealed and signed by the manager/licensee/attorney/partners
• Trade licence (copy)
• Passport of the licensee/attorney (copy)
• Duly attested power of attorney, if applicable (copy)
• Memorandum of Association, notarised and attested (copy)

CHAMBER OF COMMERCE

Each emirate has its own chamber of commerce – see the Directory for a complete list – each of which carries out a variety of activities to serve the business community, such as registering members, recording information and statistics on companies, attesting members, guiding members and facilitating members' contacts with industry members to support both local and international business networks.

PROCEDURE
WHERE: Chamber of Commerce & Industry
• Complete and submit application form for membership
• Annual fee (varies) is calculated; pay required fees
• A certificate of membership is issued (you can request an English version)

9

HOW TO...

OBTAIN A COMPANY PO BOX

You will need to organise a company PO Box as part of the set-up procedure. All mail is sent to a PO Box address, registered at your company premises. You can rent an annual company mailbox, and then use the Empost courier service and choose from a variety of bundles ('Ezimail') depending on the volumes of post arriving locally, from overseas or from further afield. The bundles include domestic courier services, weekly pick-up services and discounts on domestic unaddressed mail.

PREREQUISITES
• Aged 18 or older
• UAE resident

WHAT TO BRING
• Completed and signed Company PO Box Service application form, with company stamp (download form online from epg.gov.ae or emiratespost.gov.ae)
• Passport with Resident ID (one copy)
• Trade licence (one copy)
• Annual fees: Vary according to the bundle you select and range from Dhs.750 (company PO Box Light) up to Dhs.12,000 (Ezimail Gold bundle). Fees are calculated on a pro-rata basis. Running from 1 January to 31 December, the rate decreases each month

PROCEDURE
WHERE: Emirates Post branches
• Select post office where you would like to rent a company mailbox
• Submit all documents and fees
• Company is assigned a box number immediately
• Your PO Box key will be given to you on the spot at the branch
• Username and password will be assigned to track post online
• Track your received post online or by text message
• Renew your PO Box online at epg.gov.ae or emiratespost.ae

PO FOXED
We've heard stories of PO Boxes being assigned in parts of Dubai that are impossible to find. Be sure to confirm exactly where your PO Box is located before setting out to find it, and a contact to ask if you end up completely foxed.

10

HOW TO...

APPOINT A COMMERCIAL AGENT

A foreign company can supply goods or services from abroad in the UAE through a licensed importer on a supply-of-goods basis or through a commercial agent/distributor. The commercial agent is entitled to statutory exclusive rights to distribute and market products and goods within a certain territory; they receive a commission for services. The agent must register this agency agreement with the Ministry of Economy (MOE).

COMMERCIAL REGISTRATION DEPARTMENT

This department within the Ministry of Economy licences and registers foreign branch companies, as well as those operating in free zones. As well as approving commercial agents to be listed on a Commercial Register, it also distributes information about companies operating in the UAE in its Commercial Bulletin.

PREREQUISITES

- Agent must be a UAE national OR a wholly-owned UAE entity incorporated in the UAE
- Agent must be listed on the Ministry of Economy's Commercial Register
- A commercial agent agreement must include: name, nationality and address of agent; list of products, commodities and services covered by company; territory that the agreement covers; date on which the agreement comes into effect; duration of the agency and provisions in event of default
- If a commercial company, agreement must include company's name and description, head office, branch addresses and capital amount

WHAT TO BRING

- Agent's trade licence and MOE Commercial Register certificate (original and copy)
- Authenticated commercial agent agreement (original and copy)
- Registration fee (varies)
- Memorandum of Association (one certified/one normal)
- Passport of each partner (copy)
- Certificate proving commercial agent/company is owned by UAE nationals (original and copy)

NOTE: All documents must be translated into Arabic and certified by a notary public.

PROCEDURE

WHERE: Ministry of Economy (MOE)

- Notarise the commercial agent agreement in the UAE, or in country of principal draft
- If notarised in the country of principal draft, agreement must be attested by the UAE Embassy
- If notarised in the UAE, it must be attested by the Ministry of Foreign Affairs
- Register the agreement with the Ministry of Economy's Commercial Registration department
- Submit application form and all documents to MOE
- Pay fees (varies)
- MOE will reply within 15 days
- If accepted, agent will receive authenticated certificate confirming registration
- Details of the commercial agent agreement will be published in the MOE's Commercial Bulletin
- If declined, MOE must provide reasons for dismissal

CANCELLING A COMMERCIAL AGENT

It can be difficult to terminate an agreement with a commercial agent especially if the contract is tied to a specific timespan. You can seek termination from the Commercial Agency Committee at the Ministry of Economy, or take the matter to the UAE Courts.

Chamber of Commerce & Industry - Deira

FREE
ZONES

UNLIKE MAINLAND BUSINESSES, IN A FREE ZONE IT'S POSSIBLE TO MAINTAIN 100% FOREIGN OWNERSHIP

ADVANTAGES INCLUDE

100%

FOREIGN OWNERSHIP

THE UAE IS HOME TO MORE THAN 30 FREE TRADE ZONES

The UAE is home to more than 30 Free Trade Zones, or free zones, which were introduced by the government to encourage foreign companies to set up in the emirate by offering tax exemptions, 100% foreign ownership (elsewhere you need an equal partnership with an Emirati sponsor) and other incentives. Each free zone is designed around one or more industries such as finance, aviation and media.

Free Zone Authority

Each free zone is governed by an independent Free Zone Authority (FZA), which provides the infrastructure, ancillary services and the regulatory framework to support free zone business set-ups. Facilities available to a free zone business can include offices, warehouses, and land for development and industrial units.

You will need to apply to a specific Free Zone Authority before setting up your business, and this FZA will issue you with a trade licence; you do not need to apply to the Department of Economic Development (DED). This trade licence can be renewed annually as long as the lease agreement is in force.

Types Of Business

Each free zone has its own criteria but, in general, companies can operate in a free zone as one of the following:

- **Free Zone Establishment (FZE):** formed with a minimum of one shareholder and a maximum of 50, either individual (a person) or non-individual (a company). A minimum share capital of Dhs.1,000 is required. Each share should be in the denomination of Dhs.1,000
- **Free Zone Company (FZCO):** two or more shareholders
- **Branch office of an existing company:** a foreign company can set up a branch of its existing company in a free zone, no share capital is required
- **Free Zone Limited Liability Company (FZ-LLC):** setting up an LLC can be a slightly longer process and have a minimum capital requirement which varies from free zone to free zone
- **Sole proprietorship/freelancer:** operate as a freelance professional, in other words a sole practitioner who conducts business in their birth name as opposed to a brand name

Rules & Regulations

The rules and procedures for establishing companies in free zones differ from the rest of the UAE, particularly with regards to foreign ownership. While mainland businesses generally require a 51% stake to be held by a UAE national sponsor, or the

FACILITIES AVAILABLE TO A FREE ZONE BUSINESS CAN INCLUDE OFFICES, WAREHOUSES, AND LAND FOR DEVELOPMENT AND INDUSTRIAL UNITS

employment of a local service agent, in a free zone it's possible to maintain 100% foreign ownership.

There are exceptions to this rule, however. To sell your products in the UAE, you will need to use a commercial agent (see Appointing a commercial agent). To conduct business on the mainland you will need to apply for an additional licence from the DED; the process and costs are essentially the same as if setting up a business on the mainland in the first place.

Law Changes

Another thing to bear in mind is that a recently proposed law change, that has subsequently been rejected, would have made 100% foreign ownership of companies on the mainland possible. Should this ever resurface and be put into law, the reasons for being in a free zone may be diminished to your specific business.

The common legal forms for free zone entities to conduct business in the rest of the UAE are civil work company, limited liability company, or branch. A UAE local service agent will need to be appointed for a civil work company or branch; a limited liability company requires the sponsorship of a UAE national (with a 51% share of the company). Anyone conducting economic activities outside the free zone will be fined up to Dhs.100,000.

Labour and immigration laws vary slightly between free zones. The following rules are also worth considering:

- All businesses operating in a free zone must have a physical presence in the free zone
- All businesses must operate under UAE Labour Law, and employees must be sponsored as a UAE resident
- Each free zone will enforce a limit on the number of shareholders and directors of an LLC, although these can reside anywhere in the world
- Typically, the general manager must reside within the UAE as he/she will be the day-to-day point of contact for all matters concerning the free zone business
- All businesses most open a corporate PO Box (see How To... No.9)

It is imperative to consider fully what your business plan will require before deciding on a mainland or a free zone set-up, as you could waste time and money if you realise later that you made the wrong choice. Deposits paid to Free Zone Authorities are not refundable, so it's your responsibility to be informed about all the legal aspects of incorporating a business within a free zone.

Advantages

The advantages of setting up a company wholly inside a free zone include:

- Option of having 100% foreign ownership of the business
- Waiver of corporate tax for 15 years; this can be renewed for another 15 years upon expiry not withstanding any subsequent change to federal or local laws
- Import and export tax exemptions of up to 100%
- Personal income tax waiver
- Documentation is less and is mostly in English
- Set-up can usually be quicker
- Repatriation of capital and profits up to 100%
- Assistance in recruiting labour, assistance in sponsorship and housing and other support services

Getting started

Each free zone is designed around one or more industry and offers licences to companies working within them. The free zones will also have offices and warehouses that are specifically built considering the requirement of the type of business that is approved in that free zone.

For example, the Khalifa Industrial Zone Abu Dhabi (KIZAD) will provide a huge industrial park set up for foreign large-scale and downstream manufacturing companies with a huge port to facilitate imports of materials and exports of goods. The Abu Dhabi government estimates that this one free zone will account for as much as 15% of its non-oil GDP by 2030, so the significance of free zones should not be underestimated.

Freelancers

The route to freelancing in the UAE is also through a free zone. A freelance permit enables you to trade in your birth name rather than a registered business name, and many free zones around the country offer freelance permits. See the section on Freelance later in this chapter for more information.

Free Zone ID

Employees working within a free zone will either be issued a labour card or a free zone ID, valid for one to three years. The FZA will process all residence visas directly through the General Directorate of Residency and Foreigners Affairs (GDRFA), without having to get approval from the Ministry of Labour. This speeds up the process and visas can often be processed within hours. Once the GDRFA has stamped a residence visa, the free zone will then issue the labour card or free zone ID.

11

HOW TO...

SET UP IN A FREE ZONE

The criteria for setting up in different free zones vary, but the procedures remain more or less the same.

PREREQUISITES
- Minimum capital requirement is set by each individual FZA

WHAT TO BRING
- Application form downloaded from free zone website
- Passport and residence visa (copy) of shareholders and managers
- Business plan template
- Board resolution and/or power of attorney for the manager – must state the manager's full name as per passport

PROCEDURE
WHERE: Relevant Free Zone Authority (FZA)
- Check with the free zone to see which licences it supports
- Applicant deals with the FZA on the premises
- For a fee, FZA will assist with visas, permits and UAE government paperwork
- Submit application for registration online

If approved
- Submit all paperwork to the relevant FZA
- Pay required application fees
- Open a corporate bank account
- Open a company PO Box
- Deposit minimum capital amount (not required for branch company)
- Submit proof of capital letter to FZA
- Licence and lease is prepared (two days)
- Sign sponsorship agreement and lease agreement
- Collect licence (and keys if applicable)

ADDITIONAL COSTS
Utilities and maintenance are usually included in the rental cost but it pays to double check. Signboard costs can also be included, otherwise will cost around Dhs.500. Car parking charges, if not included, can cost up to Dhs.1,000 per month.

COSTS
These are approximate figures only:
Annual licence fee: Dhs.10,000 – 30,000
Processing fee: Dhs.500
Office rental: Dhs.1,200 – 2,400 per square metre
Insurance: Dhs.1,500 per month
Registration fee: Dhs.10,000
PO Box charges: Dhs.350 – 1,000

Dubai Free Zones

The following is a list of free zones in Dubai that are of interest to start-ups and SMEs.

Dubai Airport Free Zone (DAFZA)

dafz.ae

Offers free zone establishments or branch offices of existing companies state-of-the-art facilities and comprehensive business support. At the end of 2013 DAFZA reduced the minimum capital required for each shareholder to Dhs.1,000 per shareholder. Its SME setup allows for sole proprietorship or up to 50 shareholders. Set-up options including provision of a furnished 50 sq m workspace, with four workstations and a meeting room, start at Dhs.12,000 per month. Investors can opt for a smaller space with monthly rent starting at Dhs.4,000 per month.

Dubai Auto Zone (DAZ)

ezw.ae

DAZ is managed by Jebel Ali Free Zone Authority. It was established with the objective of re-exporting cars to the Asia and Africa regions. This zone comprises one million square metres of bonded area and has easy access to all airports and seaports in the region.

Dubai Biotech Research Park (DuBiotech)

dubiotech.ae

DuBiotech aims to facilitate an environment for networking and collaboration within the biotech community by offering products such as office space, laboratory space, land area for manufacturing and research and development operations. The presence of hotels, retail, a hospital, schools, safety and security measures, as well as residential facilities ensure a quality lifestyle within the park.

Dubai Flower Centre (DFC)

dubaiairport.com

Strategically located at Dubai International Airport, the Dubai Flower Centre is a new hub of growth for the floriculture industry in the 21st century. With innovative logistics and commercial solutions, DFC enables the industry to reduce transit times, improve quality and grow profits.

Dubai Healthcare City (DHCC)

dhcc.ae

Home to many major international healthcare brands, with over 120 medical facilities and 4,000 healthcare professionals.

DAZ WAS ESTABLISHED WITH THE OBJECTIVE OF RE-EXPORTING CARS TO THE ASIA AND AFRICA REGIONS

Dubai International Academic City (DIAC)
diacedu.com
A global academic destination that provides all institutions housed in it with opportunities for communication, experience-sharing and cooperation to utilise latest technologies and processes. Freelance permits are available.

Dubai International Financial Centre (DIFC)
difc.ae
This federal financial free zone provides a platform for business and financial institutions to work together across the region. It has over 1,000 active registered firms, including 21 of the world's top 25 banks, 11 of the top 20 money managers, six of the world's 10 largest insurers, and six out of 10 top law firms in the world. It also has the DIFC Courts, an independent common law judiciary based in DIFC with jurisdiction over civil and commercial disputes in or relating to DIFC.

Dubai Internet City (DIC)
dubaiinternetcity.com
Established in 2000, Dubai Internet City is the largest ICT hub in the Middle East. Home to global names such as Facebook and LinkedIn, it is also the location for some of the region's most

Dubai Media City

dynamic and successful technology SMEs and start-up organisations. DIC is one of a group of free zones that falls under the auspices of the Dubai Technology & Media Free Zone Authority (TECOM).

Dubai Knowledge Village (DKV)
tecom.ae

A free zone dedicated to educational establishments and institutions located within the Dubai Technology & Media Free Zone Authority.

Dubai Logistics City
dwc.ae

The Logistics District offers direct access to air, sea and road transportation, including a dedicated airport-seaport corridor that allows cargo to be moved from port to airport in just 20 minutes. It also offers simplified start-up procedures, minimal bureaucracy and is competitively priced. Moreover, the district's corporate occupants can opt for either free zone or non-bonded zone licensing.

Dubai Maritime City
dubaimaritimecity.ae

Built in 2008, DMC was built on 2.27 million square metres of reclaimed land and is the world's first purpose-built maritime centre. The marine-centric free zone is located near Port Rashid.

Dubai Media City (DMC)
dubaimediacity.com

Since 2001, Dubai Media City has hosted both global and regional media companies as a free zone in Dubai. The following sectors may apply to become a part of DMC: advertising and communication, media and marketing services, media support services, event management, event support services, media consultancy, new media, freelancers and associations (nonprofit). DMC also falls under the auspices of Dubai Technology & Media Free Zone Authority.

Dubai Multi Commodities Centre (DMCC)
dmcc.ae

The Dubai Multi Commodities Centre is a free zone authority for Jumeirah Lakes Towers, or JLT Free Zone, one of the largest free zone developments in Dubai. The 200-hectare mixed-use free zone was established in 2002 as a strategic initiative by the government of Dubai to provide the physical, market and financial infrastructure required to set up a commodities market place in Dubai.

SINCE 2001, DUBAI MEDIA CITY HAS HOSTED BOTH GLOBAL AND REGIONAL MEDIA COMPANIES AS A FREE ZONE IN DUBAI

DUBAI STUDIO CITY IS A MODERN FACILITY INTEGRATING EVERY COMPONENT UNDER ONE ROOF. SPREAD ACROSS 22 MILLION SQUARE FEET, IT INCLUDES PRODUCTION, POST-PRODUCTION, EQUIPMENT RENTAL, BUSINESS CENTRE AND SATELLITE FACILITIES

Dubai Outsource Zone (DOZ)

doz.ae

Dubai Outsource Zone (DOZ) is a base for companies that provide mid to high-end outsourcing services and captives as well as serving as an offshore centre for disaster recovery facilities. DOZ is well-positioned to cater to offshoring requirements from Europe, the US, the Middle East, Asia and Africa. Some of the key sectors that can thrive in DOZ are call centres, IT, finance, insurance, healthcare, logistics, tourism, real estate, and energy with knowledge processes, research and development, and business continuity and planning as the primary outsource functions.

Dubai Silicon Oasis Authority (DSOA)

dsoa.ae

Established in 2004, the 7.2 kilometre squared Dubai Silicon Oasis is a living and working integrated community with free trade zone incentives and benefits for its companies operating within the tech park. A large capital investment in its infrastructure, it caters to the needs of the high-tech industries operating in this zone.

Dubai Studio City (DSC)

dubaistudiocity.ae

Designed to accelerate the growth of the broadcast, film, television and music production industries, Dubai Studio City is a modern facility integrating every component under one roof. Spread across 22 million square feet, it includes production, post-production, equipment rental, business centre and satellite facilities among others. Companies can lease office space and studios as well as plots of land to build their own infrastructure, and the free zone is home to some of Dubai's most popular radio stations. There are three types of spaces available on lease: commercial offices, boutique studios and residential units.

Dubai Textile City (DTC)

texmas.com

DTC offers warehousing, showroom and office space to the textile industry in 250 units over two million square feet. The idea is to promote the textile trade in Dubai and to enhance the image of Dubai as the largest and most convenient textile trading hub in the region.

ENPARK

enpark.ae

Established in 2006, the Energy and Environment Park (ENPARK), a member of TECOM Investments, is a dedicated free zone for clean energy and environmental technology. ENPARK features manufacturing companies with environmentally-friendly production lines, residential communities and retail space, including shopping, dining, and entertainment outlets. The commercial component of ENPARK includes expansive open areas, niche business centres and office space.

Gold and Diamond Park (DGDP)
goldanddiamondpark.com
Established in May 2001, this free zone – located in Al Qouz – is an extension of the Jebel Ali Free Zone. The park attracts leading jewellery manufacturers from around the world, and manufacturing units supplying gold and diamond jewellery to retailers.

International Humanitarian City
ihc.ae
An independent free zone authority created by the Government of Dubai, IHC consolidates Dubai as an essential link in the humanitarian value chain. IHC addresses the specific needs of the humanitarian aid and development community, while grouping them in a secure environment that fosters partnerships, social responsibility and global change.

Acting both as an operational platform and a physical and virtual meeting place, IHC provides nonprofit organisations, companies, donors, volunteers, governments and those striving to save lives with a common ground for collaboration.

Jebel Ali Free Zone Authority (JAFZA)
jafza.ae
Established in 1985, JAFZA covers an enormous 48 km2 at the southern end of the city of Dubai, and is home to over 6,100 companies. As one of the world's largest and fastest-growing free zones, it provides office units, warehouses, light industrial units or land for businesses. Various company types may be formed within JAFZA, including Free Zone Establishments (FZE), Free Zone Companies (FZCO), Branch Companies and Special Status Non-Resident Offshore Companies.

Dubai Techno Park (DTP)
technopark.ae
TechnoPark is being built on 21 million square metres of land, and will house 60,000 permanent residents and employ over 133,000 people. It will function as a hub that enables research partners to access the resources of academic and research institutions, and international associations worldwide.

JAFZA COVERS AN ENORMOUS 48 KM2 AT THE SOUTHERN END OF THE CITY OF DUBAI, AND IS HOME TO OVER 6,400 COMPANIES

TWOFOUR54'S VISION IS TO POSITION ABU DHABI AS A REGIONAL CENTRE OF EXCELLENCE IN CONTENT CREATION ACROSS ALL MEDIA PLATFORMS INCLUDING FILM, BROADCAST, MUSIC, DIGITAL MEDIA, EVENTS, GAMING AND PUBLISHING

Abu Dhabi Free Zones

The free zones of Abu Dhabi include the pioneering green city of Masdar, and holistic solutions for the media industry.

Masdar City

masdarcityfreezone.com

Masdar City is the first global cleantech cluster to be located in one of the most sustainable cities in the world. It is home to the Masdar Institute of Science and Technology and the International Renewable Energy Agency (IRENA).

Masdar City offers all the benefits one would associate with a special economic zone, though with a unique focus on clean technology and renewables, in a business-friendly and entrepreneurial environment right next to Abu Dhabi International Airport.

twofour54

twofour54.com

Named after the geographical co-ordinates of Abu Dhabi, twofour54's vision is to position Abu Dhabi as a regional centre of excellence in content creation across all media platforms including film, broadcast, music, digital media, events, gaming and publishing. twofour54's aim is to create a collaborative and

Masdar City

supportive campus community; stimulating creative and professional partnerships through three key business pillars: tadreeb – the training academy; ibtikar – innovation & support; and intaj – state-of-the-art production facilities.

Industrial City Abu Dhabi (ICAD)

zonescorp.com

Run by the Higher Corporation for Specialised Economic Zones (ZonesCorp), ICAD is split into five sections, each covering specific industries, including heavy to light manufacturing, engineering and processing. The latest, ICAD IV and ICAD V cover technology and light industries and the automobile industry respectively.

Khalifa Industrial Zone (KIZAD)

kizad.com

Kizad's world-class infrastructure, transportation and logistics options, as well as its low operating cost environment is something they believe will not only promote business efficiency but also make it easier for you to achieve your business goals.

Kizad is a huge industrial zone and port centrally situated between Abu Dhabi and Dubai, and is the ideal location for businesses to tap into huge regional and global markets.

Abu Dhabi Airports Company (ADAC)

adac.ae

Established in 2006, the owner and operator of Abu Dhabi International Airport is set to establish a logistics park next to the airport which is planned to operate as a free zone facility called Abu Dhabi Airport Free Zone (ADFZ). Its creation marks a milestone in Abu Dhabi's plans to establish itself as a dynamic business centre. The logistics park will take advantage of Abu Dhabi International Airport's strategic geographical position on the crossroads between east and west, and the large-scale economic development of the emirate.

Al Ain Industrial City (AAIC)

zonescorp.com

Another run by the Higher Corporation for Specialised Economic Zones (ZonesCorp), the location is ideal for any company looking for easy access to both Dubai and Abu Dhabi, as well as Sharjah. AAIC is divided into the following categories: light manufacturing (textiles, paper, wood industries) and repair workshops; agricultural processing and food canning; construction materials; technology; environmental industries.

THE SHARJAH AIRPORT INTERNATIONAL FREE ZONE (SAIF-ZONE) WAS SET UP IN 1995 AND NOW SERVICES OVER 2,900 COMPANIES FROM 91 COUNTRIES

Northern Emirates Free Zones

Several free zones in the UAE's smaller emirates offer competitive concessions for start-ups.

Sharjah Airport Free Zone (SAIF-Zone)

saif-zone.com

The Sharjah Airport International Free Zone (SAIF-ZONE) was set up in 1995 and now services over 2,900 companies from 91 countries. Covering a wide cross section of industry, companies include some of the biggest names in the field of IT services, media, consumer durables, and light to medium manufacturing, among several others.

Hamriyah Free Zone (HFZ)

hfza.ae

The free zone manages an area of approximately 22 million sq m of industrial and commercial land and a 14 metre deep port which includes scope for expansion. It offers office units, land and pre-built warehouses, too. Aimed at SMEs, Hamriyah is split into seven distinct zones: Oil and Gas Zone, Petrochemical Zone, Steel City, Construction World, Timber Land, Maritime City and Perfume Land.

Ras Al Khaimah Free Trade Zone (RAKFTZ)

rakftz.com

Ras Al Khaimah Free Trade Zone Authority has created a system of four unique Free Zone Parks that should suit most investor requirements. The concept includes the Business Park, Industrial Park, Technology Park and Al Ghail Park, offering the offices, equipped warehouses and facilities needed. These are situated at different locations across the emirate.

RAK Maritime City

rakmaritimecity.ae

RAKMC Free Zone issues both free zone enterprise (FZE) and free zone company (FZCo) licences. RAKMC is also zoned into areas for specified uses: retail, warehousing, general cargo handling, industrial production and manufacturing, and ship building and repairs. Lease agreements are offered for 25 years, renewable for a further 25 years. Longer leases are considered for periods up to 99 years.

Fujairah Free Zone (FFZ)

fujairahfreezone.ae

FFZ offers three types of licence: Trading & General Trading Licence authorizes the import, export and re-export of agreed and specified commodities. The licence entitles the investor to carry out import, export and re-export freely in the free zone and outside the UAE. For local distribution, the FZA can arrange special permits with the relevant government departments. A Warehousing Licence can be obtained on leasing warehousing facilities and entitles the investor to use the warehouse as a hub for major distribution, benefiting storage and packaging of goods. Lastly, a Manufacturing Licence is obtained on approval and implementation of the project. All projects must be fully insured including manpower and machinery.

Fujairah Creative City
fmg.ae

Creative City is a completely new media innovation cluster and an addition to the media-hubs in the region after Dubai Media City and twofour54 of Abu Dhabi. Creative City is targeting smaller players who are trying to establish new businesses or benefit from a new location for their existing operations. Creative City, having 40,000 square metres of dedicated land area, will complement existing media clusters in the region, and further facilitate creativity in all fields, for both freelancers as well as companies in a variety of specialties, such as training, media production, media services and technology.

Ajman Free Zone (AFZ)
afza.gov.ae

A massive multi-million dirham development plan on over a million square metre area is under progress at the free zone, which on completion will be able to accommodate 1,500 companies.

Strategically situated at the entrance of the Arabian Gulf, Ajman Free Zone is well placed to serve the eastern and western markets. Ajman's proximity to Sharjah and Dubai provides easy accessibility to the two international airports and four ports. Ajman Port, serving over 1,000 vessels in a year, has emerged as an important maritime focal point today. It has twelve berths. A massive development plan for Ajman Ports, under progress, seeks to enhance its facilities to world level in the near future.

Ahmed Bin Rashid Free Zone (ABRFZ)
06 765 5882

Phase one of this Umm Al Quwain development has 34 light industries units, a mess hall and accommodation for a modest labour force. The free zone complex consists of 845 metres of quay wall and 118,000 square metres of land reserved for light industrial development. General trading, manufacturing and consultancy are the permitted activities in this free zone with office leases available annually and 15 year leases for industrial units.

CREATIVE CITY IS TARGETING SMALLER PLAYERS WHO ARE TRYING TO ESTABLISH NEW BUSINESSES OR BENEFIT FROM A NEW LOCATION FOR THEIR EXISTING OPERATIONS

"FREE ZONES PROVIDE A ONE-WINDOW OPERATION FOR BUSINESS NEEDS"

Samer Qudah
Business Al Tamimi
Web tamimi.com
Activities Corporate law

Having joined Al Tamimi in 1999, Samer Qudah has wide ranging experience advising major blue chip organisations and government concerns as well as SMEs on a wide range of issues, including legal due diligence, joint ventures, commercial agreements, regulatory affairs, e-commerce, privacy and other issues.

What are the most important legal factors to consider when setting up in a free zone?
The main purpose of free zones within the UAE is to facilitate an environment whereby corporate entities can be established by foreign investors with maximum ease. Free zones provide a one-window operation for the needs of the investor, such as licensing corporate entities, provision of offices, employee visa sponsorship and so on. The most important legal factors to take into account are as follows:

- **Business activity.** Each free zone has a prescribed list of activities that they provide licenses for. An investor must choose a free zone that accommodates their business activity. Also, free zone corporate entities cannot conduct commercial activities outside of the free zone, therefore this is something to bear in mind should you wish to do business into mainland UAE.

Any Advice?
The most imperative starting point is determining the objective of incorporating an entity in the free zone, and the proposed business activity the free zone entity on the ground will conduct. Once this is resolved, the second step is to select an appropriate free zone.

- **Legal form.** Based on the investor's proposed business activity, the appropriate legal form should also be taken into consideration. The majority of the free zones offer the option of either incorporating a Limited Liability Company (LLC) or establishing a branch office. However, in law a branch office is merely an extension of its parent company and has no separate legal identity and thus can only conduct activities that are permitted by its parent, under its constitutional documents.

- **Employment.** Employees under the sponsorship of a free zone entity cannot work outside of the free zone; as all expatriates in the UAE must be under the sponsorship and visa of their employer. This should be taken into account in cases where employees engage in any work required to be conducted outside of the free zone, such as installation.

What are the legal benefits of setting up in a free zone?
The obvious advantage of setting up in a free zone is that it offers 100% ownership by foreign investors. In a free zone, LLCs can be incorporated with only one shareholder, whereas in Dubai mainland it is mandatory that two or more shareholders should set up an LLC. I have set out below numerous other benefits of setting up in a free zone:

- No local sponsor, partner or service agent required
- Permitted corporate structure includes branch of a foreign company and free zone incorporated companies, with one or more than one shareholder
- Statutory exemption from corporate taxes
- Exemption from duties on import, subject to the items imported being used or consumed in the free zone
- No restrictions on repatriation of capital and profits
- No currency restrictions
- Simplified licensing procedure and registration facilities
- A simple employee sponsorship system
- Option to lease and develop land according to one's own needs
- Option to lease new offices with modern infrastructure facilities
- Prestigious address

What are the main legal restrictions of setting up in a free zone?
The main restriction to note is that an entity incorporated within the free zone cannot do any retailing or direct trade with persons in the mainland, and can only do so through a distributor that is licensed in the mainland. However, this restriction is not applied in cases whereby the entity is providing services, and only in scenarios wherein tangible goods are being transferred.

What legal tips do you have for starting a business in a free zone?
Based on experience, these are the main factors to consider:

- The available activities and licences offered by the free zone
- The costs for setting up within the free zone
- The registration time frame
- Licensing fees, lease and other required fees
- Availability for office premises
- Any other specific incentives provided by such free zone

Other factors to consider are the maturity and credibility of the free zone and the geographical location of the free zone.

AN ENTITY INCORPORATED WITHIN A FREE ZONE CANNOT DO ANY RETAILING OR DIRECT TRADE WITH PERSONS IN THE MAINLAND

OFFSHORE
BUSINESS

AN OFFSHORE COMPANY DOES NOT HAVE THE TAX LIABILITIES OF ITS HOME JURISDICTION AS IT IS BASED 'OFFSHORE'. GENERALLY, CONFIDENTIALITY IS MUCH GREATER TOO

OFFSHORE BUSINESSES CAN HAVE 100% FOREIGN OWNERSHIP

JAFZ, RAKIC AND RAKIA ARE THE UAE'S OFFSHORE JURISDICTIONS

An offshore company, also known as an international business company (IBC), can operate as any other company. It can enter into contracts, open bank accounts, purchase and sell various products and services, and own property. The main difference is that it does not have the tax liabilities of its home jurisdiction as it is based 'offshore'. Generally, confidentiality is much greater too.

However, that doesn't exempt the company from paying taxes in the countries that it does business in and it must not operate within the country that it is incorporated in. In other words, you could set up an offshore company in the United Arab Emirates to take advantage of the tax benefits and to establish a reputation enhancing presence in the region, but you can't trade within the UAE.

There are some other advantages to setting up an offshore company in the UAE too. The EU Savings Directive now means that all financial institutions in EU member states must disclose tax and bank information to the relevant tax authorities. To avoid this, traditional tax havens in the EU can charge customers significant fees to maintain discretion. In the UAE, this is not applicable, meaning companies and high net worth individuals can maintain privacy without additional costs as there is no public register of shareholders and directors.

Offshore Company Jurisdictions

Dubai is the key destination for those looking to establish an offshore company in the UAE. Jebel Ali Free Zone (JAFZ) is the one jurisdiction where this is possible thanks to the 2003 Jebel Ali Free Zone Offshore Companies Regulations.

For those setting up in JAFZ, the company name must end with the word 'Limited' and the company must have a minimum of one shareholder and two directors (corporate directors are not permitted). The process involves submitting an application for a certificate for incorporation along with articles of association specifying regulations for the offshore company to the registrar.

If the registrar grants approval, the offshore company receives its certificate of incorporation and is ready to start conducting its business.

The advantages of setting up in Jebel Ali Free Zone are:
- No taxes to pay (aside from oil producing companies or branches of foreign banks)
- 100% foreign ownership

DUBAI IS THE KEY DESTINATION FOR THOSE LOOKING TO ESTABLISH AN OFFSHORE COMPANY IN THE UAE. JEBEL ALI FREE ZONE IS THE ONE JURISDICTION WHERE THIS IS POSSIBLE

THERE ARE SOME RESTRICTIONS: A DUBAI OFFSHORE COMPANY MUST HAVE A REGISTERED OFFICE AND LOCAL AGENT, THE LATTER BEING APPROVED BY THE LOCAL AUTHORITIES

- No taxation information exchange agreements with other countries
- No public register of shareholders and directors
- Confidential banking system in the UAE that's ideal for meeting requirements of high net worth investors
- Can own Dubai property (since 2011 other offshore companies cannot own Dubai property, but can own property in the rest of the UAE)
- Can hold a UAE bank account for conducting routine operational transactions
- Can trade internationally
- Low set up costs (with annual fees)

There are however some restrictions: a Dubai offshore company must have a registered office and local agent, the latter being approved by the local authorities. Names of companies must not include the following words either: Banking, Insurance and Re-insurance, as these services are not allowed to be offered by offshore companies.

A company formed in JAFZ also cannot do business within the UAE (even within a free zone) aside from the following instances:

- Making or maintaining professional contact with legal consultants, accountants, management companies or other similar entities doing business in the UAE
- Preparing and maintaining books and records within the UAE

However, if an offshore company does wish to conduct trade or other business in the free zone or elsewhere in the UAE, then it can obtain the appropriate licence to the specific activity it wants to undertake from the competent authorities.

There are also two other jurisdictions in the UAE that allow the formation of offshore companies, both of which are in Ras Al Khaimah; Ras Al Khaimah Investment Company (RAKIC) and Ras Al Khaimah Investment Authority (RAKIA). The regulations regarding offshore company incorporation and the advantages of setting up here are similar to in Dubai, however, RAKIC also allows shareholders to opt for their preferred jurisdiction of law in relation to certain matters, such as succession, and disputes between shareholders.

Offshore Companies Away From The UAE

There's nothing to stop you from setting up an offshore company away from the UAE, such as the British Virgin Isles, Seychelles or any number of popular jurisdictions. Each can have its own advantages and disadvantages, and may be particularly attractive when it comes to avoiding the UAE's complicated inheritance laws.

British Virgin Islands
British Virgin Islands (BVI) is one of the oldest offshore jurisdictions in the world. The number of companies registered on BVI has grown to over 450,000. BVI offshore companies are exempted from all taxes and stamp duties.

The company incorporation documents of a BVI company do not carry the name or identity of any shareholder or director. The time taken to complete the incorporation of a BVI Company is just three working days. BVI companies are also offered legal asset protection. The shareholder(s) and director(s) of the company can be an individual person or a corporate body.

Cayman Islands
The Cayman Islands is a British Overseas Territory located in the western Caribbean Sea. These islands are a global offshore commercial hub and the fifth largest banking centre in the world.

When setting up from the Cayman Islands, a minimum of one shareholder and director is required. Nominee shareholders and directors are permitted. The Cayman Islands offers legal asset protection, low operational costs and no minimum capital requirement.

Companies registered in Cayman Islands are subject to the following restrictions: no business is permitted within Cayman Islands; no banking, insurance or reinsurance activities are permitted; cannot deal with trusteeship business or investment schemes.

Seychelles
The independent republic of Seychelles has registered over 70,000 companies to date and is one of the world's most progressive offshore financial centres. It takes up to four working days to complete the incorporation of a Seychelles company. The shareholder(s) and director(s) of the company can be a person or a corporate body. A minimum of one shareholder and director is required. Nominee shareholders and directors are permitted. Seychelles offers no local taxation, legal asset protection and no minimum capital requirement.

Companies registered in Seychelles are subject to the same restrictions as those in the Cayman Islands.

ONLINE
BUSINESS

WITH EXCELLENT INTERNET COVERAGE IN MUCH OF THE COUNTRY AND A HUGE PROLIFERATION OF SMARTPHONES, E-COMMERCE IS A GREAT OPPORTUNITY FOR ANY FLEDGLING BUSINESS

ONLINE SALES ARE EXPECTED TO GROW BY

95%

IN THE UAE

VIRTUAL OFFICES ARE AVAILABLE THROUGHOUT THE COUNTRY

Online retail is a fast growing area in the United Arab Emirates' economy. Over the five-year period leading to 2018, it's expected that the volume of online sales will grow by a massive 95%. With excellent internet coverage in much of the country and a huge proliferation of smartphones, e-commerce is a great opportunity for any fledgling business.

Like any business though, certain laws need to be adhered too. A trade licence is still needed from the Department of Economy (DED) for the mainland or from a Free Zone Authority if you're setting up within a free zone, and this licence still needs to be in line with what you are offering. For example, if you're planning on selling goods to UAE customers then you'll need a commercial trading licence. Rules in free zones would mean you'd need to appoint a local service agent if selling to UAE customers.

If you're importing goods to sell in the UAE, then you'll also need to be registered with the appropriate ports and customs authority in order to get an importer's code. A 5% import tax will be applied to your imported goods unless you're selling within the free zone that your online business is based in, or if you're selling abroad.

YOU DON'T NEED A PHYSICAL ADDRESS IN ORDER TO HAVE AN ONLINE BUSINESS IN MOST EMIRATES, BUT IN DUBAI YOU DO. VIRTUAL OFFICES ARE AVAILABLE THROUGHOUT THE COUNTRY

Logistics

You don't need a physical address in order to have an online business in most emirates, but in Dubai you do. Virtual offices are available throughout the country, with global companies like Regus (regus.co.uk) offering a full range of options, while in some free zones hot desks are available.

Should you be dealing with goods, storage and delivery is also important to think about and is likely to require physical premises. For storage facilities, the process would be similar to that for any business looking for a commercial premises and is covered elsewhere in this guide. For deliveries, there are plenty of courier companies available to use, however it may be worth considering getting your own vans and drivers. While the outlay can be high, it may be a more efficient way to get goods ordered online to your customers.

Payments

Traditionally, online payments have been an issue, with goods often being paid for in cash upon delivery. This obviously creates an issue for some retailers who are made to wait for payment, and it can create additional costs if goods need to be returned. However, credit card payments online are possible and the online payment gateway PayPal is now available in the UAE, which can make the process a little more straightforward.

12

HOW TO...

OBTAIN A UAE DOMAIN NAME

You can register your domain name through Etisalat (etisalat.ae) which handles domain name registration through UAEnic (United Arab Emirates Network Information Center), or through du (du.ae) which is an accredited registrar of the .ae Domain Administration (.aeDA). It can also register other top-level domains such as those ending with .com and .net.

PREREQUISITES
- UAE resident
- Trade licence
- Domain names must: have minimum of two and a maximum of 63 characters; begin with a letter or a number and end with a letter or a number; use the English character set and may contain letters (i.e., a-z, A-Z), numbers (i.e. 0-9) and dashes (-) or a combination of these; neither begin with, nor end with a dash; not contain a dash in the third and fourth positions (e.g. ab- -cd.ae); not include a space (e.g. ab cd.ae)

WHAT TO BRING
- Passport with residence visa of company owner or sponsor (copies)
- Trade licence signed by power of attorney (copy)
- Required domain name
- Company stamp

WEBSITE
Obviously an online business needs a good website. That is, it not only needs to look good and promote your brand strongly, it also needs to be easy to navigate, readily updatable with new products and have a good system in place for order processing and payment. It's worth investing in a good initial design, as a badly ordered and difficult to use website will put potential customers off.

PROCEDURE
WHERE: Etisalat or du
- Download domain name application form at etisalat.ae or du.ae
- Pay fees, which range from Dhs.150 for one year for a .ae address to Dhs.750 for five years

GO
FREELANCE

A FREELANCE WORK PERMIT FROM A FREE ZONE ALLOWS YOU TO LIVE AND WORK IN THE UAE UNDER THE SPONSORSHIP OF THAT FREE ZONE AUTHORITY

A FREELANCE PERMIT COSTS
Dhs.20k
OR MORE

YOU CAN CONDUCT BUSINESS IN YOUR BIRTH NAME

Freelancing is legal in the UAE, and you can set yourself up as a full-time freelancer. You can pick and choose the jobs you accept and work your own hours, but you will not receive benefits such as medical insurance, sick leave or holiday pay.

To work as a freelancer, you will need a residence visa and a freelance work permit. You can get a temporary work permit if you are to be employed by a mainland company for a maximum six-month contract. Alternatively, if you are working full-time you can also apply for a part-time work permit with a second employer; you will need an NOC from your existing employer though. The easiest, most flexible option though is to get a freelance work permit from a free zone, which allows you to live and work in the UAE under the sponsorship of that FZA.

Freelance Permits

Freelancers are granted a freelance permit, which identifies you as a sole practitioner and enables you to conduct your business in your birth name as opposed to a brand name. You will also be given a UAE residence visa. Both the permit and visa are valid for one year. This typically costs between Dhs.20,000-30,000.

Once accepted as a sole proprietor, you can carry out the specific business activities printed on your licence. There are set-up costs involved, including a Dhs.5,000 deposit, and you will have to pay the Dhs.2,500 licence fee and Dhs.2,200 visa fee. You also have to renew your licence annually.

Freelancers can apply for a work permit and residence visa from a select number of free zones in the UAE, including International Media Production Zone, Dubai Media City, Dubai Technology and Media Free Zone, twofour54 and Fujairah Creative Zone.

A permit includes a residence visa, access to shared work stations and a shared PO Box address. You will need to submit a business plan, spend a minimum of three hours per week at a hot desk (but less than four hours per day), and pay around Dhs.22,000 in fees.

Another option is to apply to Virtuzone, which operates in the Fujairah Creative City free zone. Virtuzone (vz.ae) can help you set up a small company or relocate it to the UAE. Start-up costs begin at around Dhs.10,000 and significantly there's no need for a UAE sponsor. Also, there's no requirement to take a commercial premises – something that really drives up the price of setting up in other free zones.

THERE ARE SET-UP COSTS INVOLVED, INCLUDING A DHS.5,000 DEPOSIT, AND YOU WILL HAVE TO PAY THE DHS.2,500 LICENCE FEE AND DHS.2,200 VISA FEE. YOU ALSO HAVE TO RENEW YOUR LICENCE ANNUALLY

"THERE'S A STEADY STREAM OF WORK FOR RESOURCEFUL JOURNOS"

Peter Shaw-Smith
Business Freelancer writer
Activities Journalism

Peter Shaw-Smith has been a freelance writer in Dubai for just over four years. His work is mainly in shipping and aviation, as well as oil and gas, family business and family office. More generally, he also covers investments and the GCC projects market.

Where did you choose to set up your freelance licence and why?
In Dubai Media City (DMC). The DMC freelance licence allows a freelancer to operate fully as a standalone journalist throughout the UAE and beyond. In addition, DMC can help deal with red tape associated with travel throughout the GCC.

How did you find the initial set up process?
Officials at DMC Business Centre will guide you through the process. A passport copy, CV, detailed business plan (template provided), reference letters and relevant clips need to be submitted, as well as supporting letters issued by editors of publications for whom the applicant intends to work.

In my case, the promise in September 2012 of an application process lasting one month eventually resulted in a wait of four months for my visa to be issued.

How much did it cost to set up? And what services do you get?
A visa for three years' duration with DMC costs in the region of US$14,000. This is split more or less equally over three years, with a major payment at the beginning of each year, and a smaller payment covering the second six-month period of each year.

You are given an official Dubai Technology and Media Free Zone Authority card. An establishment card is also issued, although this appears to have little significance. Assistance is also provided to speed up the issuance of a UAE Identity Card. The fee also covers access to a hot desk, which allows you to operate at a workstation within DMC Business Centre at any time during normal business hours.

Any Advice?
The creation of DMC spawned a kaleidoscope of publications, mostly glossy magazines. As a freelancer, you have almost unlimited options about who you can work for. But be careful, as quality varies markedly from publication to publication.

13

HOW TO...

APPLY FOR A FREELANCE VISA

To set up as a freelancer in any of the applicable free zones, your profession needs to be related to that free zone's business activities.

The process varies between free zones, so check individual websites for specific requirements and to download forms. Below is the general procedure.

WHAT TO BRING
- Application form
- Business plan (template available)
- Passport copy with residence visa
- Reference letter(s) provided by current/previous employers recommending your ability to perform a particular task
- CV and original qualification certificates and credentials
- NOC (if UAE resident) provided by sponsor allowing you to transfer the residence visa and to obtain a freelance permit
- A good standing certificate issued by your bank certifying that the individual holds a satisfactory account
- Portfolio/samples of work

PROCEDURE
WHERE: Relevant Free Zone Authority
- Submit application for provisional approval (downloadable from free zone website) and documents
- If provisional approval is granted, you will receive a customer confirmation letter
- Sign the letter and submit
- Make the required payments: freelance permit fee; visa fee; first instalment for rent or office (if applicable), plus deposit (if applicable)
- Sign the free zone sponsorship agreement
- Freelance permit and residence visa are granted
- You will then have access to a 'hot desk' and business facilities (including a PO Box address) within the free zone that sponsored you; this is basically a single desk in an office environment that can be shared with others

IN THE MEDIA
Freelance permits are predominantly media-related: artists, editors, directors, writers, engineers, producers, photographers, camera operators and technicians in the fields of film, TV, music, radio, publishing and print media.

RECRUIT &
EMPLOY

WHEN STARTING A BUSINESS, NOT ONLY DO YOU NEED TO HAVE A STRONG BUSINESS PLAN, YOU NEED TO EMPLOY THE RIGHT STAFF TO CARRY OUT YOUR VISION THE RIGHT WAY

COMPANIES OF A CERTAIN SIZE MUST EMPLOY A MINIMUM OF 5-8% UAE NATIONALS

THERE IS NO MINIMUM WAGE SET BY THE UAE GOVERNMENT

The old adage states that a company is only as good as its staff. In the UAE, with a pool of talent from across the globe, this has never been truer. When starting a business, not only do you need to have a strong business plan, you need to employ the right staff to carry out your vision the right way. It's therefore crucial to plan your staffing requirements properly and to allow time to find exactly the right employees.

The perks of living in the UAE, such as tax-free salaries and perennially sunny weather, continue to attract a highly skilled workforce, and therefore finding the right employees for your business shouldn't be a difficult process when undertaken through the right channels.

Do take care in the recruitment phase though, as the cost of finding and replacing employees can be high.

Legalities

Anyone who works in the UAE must have a residence visa, labour card or free zone ID, and Resident ID card, all of which you as an employer need to apply for (and foot the expenses).

Before you can do this, you need an establishment labour card (see How To... No.15) and, if you're planning to recruit from abroad, an establishment immigration card (see How To... No.16).

For larger companies, a public relations officer (PRO – see How To... No.14) might be needed to conduct the many processes involved to ensure the staff you employ meet all the legal formalities. The procedures a company needs to follow to obtain the above are detailed in this chapter.

Employment Contracts

There is no minimum wage set by the UAE government, but there are plenty of regulations to be mindful of when drafting an employment contract, such as the inclusion of medical insurance. An employee earning less than Dhs.4,000 per month (Dhs.3,000 with housing allowance) is not allowed to sponsor a residence visa for his or her family.

Emiratisation

Referring to the process to place more nationals in jobs in their own countries, Emiratisation requires Western companies to employ a certain quota of UAE nationals. UAE-based companies outside free zones, and of a certain size, must employ a minimum 5-8% of UAE nationals as a condition of their trade licence.

THE PERKS OF LIVING IN THE UAE, SUCH AS TAX-FREE SALARIES AND PERENNIALLY SUNNY WEATHER, CONTINUE TO ATTRACT A HIGHLY SKILLED WORKFORCE

RECRUITING & HIRING

Because of the diverse nature of its economy and being a location that attracts international talent as a desirable place to live and work, the UAE already has an extensive talent pool in all industries. Plus there is a wealth of professional talent keen to relocate to the UAE for the tax free income and lifestyle.

Ask any recruitment agency and they'll say they have a mass of CVs channelled through their websites everyday. While some industries may have specific channels for recruitment, there are also plenty of UAE-based websites that advertise vacancies for all industries and role levels, such as bayt.com and dubizzle.com, as well as the Gulf News appointments supplement (gnads4u.com) published daily except Fridays and Saturdays, or the Khaleej Times' appointments (khaleejtimes.com) everyday except Friday. These newspaper appointments are also online. The National newspaper's listings can be viewed by subscribers only.

There are any number of recruitment agencies based in the UAE to actively headhunt desirable applicants for your company. An agency will take care of advertising positions, and vetting the reponses, as well as matching job role requrements with suitable candidates already on their database. Agencies receive their fee from you as the employer.

Alternatively, your own company website and, increasingly, your social media channels are an excellent way to reach potential staff that already show an interest in what you do.

Another way to seek out talent is to ask the people in your wider personal and professional network if they are able to suggest anyone – and there's no better recommendation than a personal one from a trusted source.

Recruitment Agencies

Abu Dhabi Recruitment Services 04 262 2512
Advanced Recruitment Services 04 297 6481
Al Lujain Recruitment Services 04 227 8800
Al Vakil Recruitment Services 04 262 9600
Arabian Gulf Recruitment Services 04 282 6868, *boyden.com*
Arabian Island Recruitment 04 337 8791
Asia Gulf Recruitment Services Establishment 04 262 7676, *asiagulf.com*
BAC Middle East 04 439 8500, *bacme.com*
Bin Eid 06 568 6144, *bineid.com*
Careerline Recruitment and Training 04 351 1426, *careerlinedubai.com*
Charterhouse 02 406 9819, *charterhouseme.ae*
Cobalt Recruitment 02 611 3000, *cobaltrecruitment.com*
Domino Recruitment & Consultancy 04 390 2090

Hays Middle East 04 361 2882, *hays.ae*
Manpower Middle East 04 391 0460, *manpowergroup.ae*
Nadia Recruitment and Manpower Services 04 331 3401,
nadia-me.com
Parsons Brinckerhoff 04 376 7222, *pbworld.com*
Reach Group 04 282 4699, *reachgroup.ae*

Media (Online and Print)
Bayt.com 04 449 3100, *bayt.com*
Dubizzle.com 04 427 9778, *dubizzle.com*
emedHR.com 04 362 4749, *emedhr.com*
GNcareers.com *gncareers.com*
Gulf News *gnads4u.com*
GulfTalent.com 04 367 2084, *gulftalent.com*
Jobs.ae 04 442 5678, *jobs.ae*
Jobs-me.com *jobs-me.com*
Jobtrackme.com 04 397 7751 *jobtrackme.com*
Khaleej Times *khaleejtimes.com*
Monstergulf.com 800 017 7030, *monstergulf.com*
The National *thenational.ae*
RecruitGulf.com *recruitgulf.com*
Staffinuae.com 04 326 2003, *staffinuae.com*

14

HOW TO...

APPLY FOR A PRO CARD

Most of the larger firms in the UAE employ a Public Relations Officer (PRO). This is an individual who deals on behalf of the company with the General Directorate of Residency and Foreigners Affairs and Ministry of Labour.

The company needs to apply for a PRO card that is valid for one year and allows it to hire someone that specialises in these activities.

PREREQUISITES
• The company already has an establishment labour card and an establishment immigration card
• The PRO is already employed by the company and under its sponsorship

WHAT TO BRING
• Police clearance certificate
• Residence visa (copy)
• Two passport-sized photos
• Trade licence and immigration card (copies) for all represented companies
• Request letter in Arabic from the sponsor (on company letterhead)
• Fees: Dhs.650 (for expatriate employee) and Dhs. 350 (for UAE national employee)

PROCEDURE
WHERE: General Directorate of Residency and Foreign Affairs (GDRFA)
• Complete card application form (at typing office)
• Submit all documents and pay required fees
• Collect PRO card one week later – it is valid for one year and can be renewed with the same procedure
• Authorised company representative and sponsor must sign and stamp forms

15

HOW TO...

APPLY FOR AN ESTABLISHMENT LABOUR CARD

Before you can apply for any employment visa for your staff, you need to apply for an establishment labour card. Issued by the Ministry of Labour, this allows a company to hire staff, obtain work permits and apply for visas on behalf of its employees. The card verifies that the company is registered with the Ministry of Labour with a specific registration number.

PREREQUISITES
• Company has a trade licence and PO Box address

WHAT TO BRING
• Trade licence (with partners list for an LLC company)
• Passport copies of partners for an LLC company
• Copy of MOA for an LLC company
• Passport and Jinsiyya (family book) or Resident ID of local sponsor, applicable to a 'mainland', not free zone, company
• Passport of local service agent or UAE national sponsor (applicable to a 'mainland', not free zone, company)
• Location map in Arabic (from Municipality)
• Electricity and Water Authority bill
• Attested power of attorney declaration
• Fees: Dhs.2,000 plus typing fees

PROCEDURE
WHERE: Ministry of Labour Tas'heel Centre
• Visit a Tas'heel typing centre with the documents to complete relevant application form, then get it translated to Arabic. Add company seal and signature of all partners (if any)
• Application can also be submitted at any Ministry of Labour office
• After receiving the card you can apply for a company E-signature card (Dhs.300)

APPROVAL
The application must be submitted by the company owner, partner or PRO. An establishment labour card will be issued on the spot if approved. This is valid until you cancel your trade licence.

16

HOW TO...

APPLY FOR AN ESTABLISHMENT IMMIGRATION CARD

A company must apply for an establishment immigration card or a new immigration computer card. This card files your company with the GDRFA. Issued for three years, it allows a company to recruit staff from abroad and apply for foreign investors, partners and employment visas.

AMENDING AN ESTABLISHMENT CARD

If you make any changes to your trade licence, such as amending the name, activity, owner, local service agent, authorised signatory or legal status, then the change must also be made on both your establishment immigration card and the establishment labour card. You will need the following:

- Typed application (from Tas'heel Centre)
- Trade licence (copy)
- Addendum listing the partners' names if an LLC (copy)
- Power of attorney attested by notary public for authorised signatories (in case of changing signatory)
- Local service agent contract (in case of professional licence)
- Establishment immigration card (amended) (copy)
- E-signature card copy of sponsor and authorised signatories (if any)
- Valid municipality-registered tenancy contract

PREREQUISITES
- The company has already obtained its trade licence

WHAT TO BRING
- Partners list for an LLC company
- Copy of MOA (memorandum of association) for an LLC company
- Passport and Jinsiyya (family book) or Resident ID of local sponsor (applicable to an 'onshore', not free zone, company)
- Passport of local service agent or UAE national sponsor (applicable to an 'onshore', not free zone, company)
- Passport copies of partners for an LLC company
- Passport photos of sponsors and partners
- Copy of tenancy contract
- Location map in Arabic
- Owners' degree certificates (notarised and legalised)
- E-signature card copy of sponsor and authorised signatories (if any)
- Fees: Dhs.2,000 application fee

PROCEDURE
WHERE: Ministry of Labour Tas'heel Centre
- Application submitted by owner, partner or public relations officer (PRO) with fee
- Complete relevant documents
- Authorised person must sign the forms and seal with company stamp
- If urgent, establishment card can be collected on the same day. If not, pay a Dhs.20 courier fee to receive the establishment card within three working days

17

HOW TO...

APPLY FOR AN INDIVIDUAL LABOUR CARD

Anyone working in the UAE private sector needs a labour card. This is typically applied for by the company's PRO directly after an employee's residence visa has been approved.

Labour cards are now electronic, replacing the previous plastic format in a government system administered by Tas'heel, designed to simplify all labour related processes. With the new electronic system, employees are able to access and print their documents at any time. This includes their employment contract.

PREREQUISITES
• Employer has arranged for employee's entry permit
• Employee has passed the medical test

WHAT TO BRING
• A copy of the company's e-signature card
• Passport photo of applicant (white background)
• Employee's entry permit
• Copy of employee's medical certificate
• Employment contract signed and sealed by company (three copies)

PROCEDURE
WHERE: Ministry of Labour Tas'heel Centre
• Employer's PRO submits all documents, makes application and pays the required fees at Tas'heel centre
• All companies are required to apply for the new electronic services within 60 days at one of Tas'heel's service centres located across the UAE
• If approved, the e-labour card and employment contract will be available online to both the employer and employee
• If refused, notification of missing documents will be posted to the employer

UAE NATIONALS
As part of setting up a business in Dubai, all companies must register Emirati employees at the Ministry of Labour and the General Authority for Pension and Social Security. There is no charge for this process.

E-LABOUR CARDS
Both companies and their employees can check their work permit status on the 'e-netwasal' page of the the MOL's website, mol.gov.ae.

EMPLOYMENT CONTRACTS

Every employee and employer is required by UAE Labour Law to sign an employment contract; this should list the starting date, type of employment, location, terms and conditions, duration and the salary. Most of the terms and conditions in the contract will be determined by UAE Labour Law – working hours, public holidays, maternity leave and so on. This is a legally binding agreement that should be written in both Arabic and English.

Just like the e-labour card, all employment contracts are now electronic and can be viewed online at mol.gov.ae. Employers must apply for both the e-labour card and e-contract through eNetwasal within 60 days of the employee's entry into the UAE or start date, or else the employer will face a fine of Dhs.1,000 for each month that passes.

Pre-conditions

Going through a thorough set of checks before engaging a new employee is likely to save a company any unwelcome surprises further down the line. Some of these remain generic wherever you operate your business. These include ensuring the prospective employee is qualified to carry out the job role in question, and fulfills the essential requirements and competencies for the role. As an employer you should carry out the relevant background and reference checks to ensure an employee's experience and qualifications are legitimate.

This last point has been a particular issue in the UAE, especially now when it is relatively straightforward to obtain very convincing fraudulent academic qualification certificates through dubious internet sources.

At the same time, there are a number of pre-conditions you should consider, based on specific UAE employment laws such as sponsorship and visa requirements:

- The prospective employee should be able to obtain and retain a valid residence visa. If transferring employment from another 'onshore' UAE firm, for example, it is likely the employee will need an NOC (no objection certificate) from the company, otherwise they could face a UAE employment ban for a defined period of either six months or one year. For free zone companies – which as explained earlier are classed as offshore – the same does not apply
- Satisfactory completion of medical test for residence visa purposes
- Confirmation of the prospective employee's ability to comply with migration procedures needed by the country of origin
- Completion of security checks and police clearance
- Provision of attested copies of educational certificates (originals)
- The joining date specified, or such other date, is agreed internally by the employer and all relevant stakeholders

- Verification that you as the company hiring the employee are his/her sole employer
- Before completing an employment contract, the employer must ensure that the prospective employee has confirmed acceptance of the employment offer in writing

Employment Contracts

From time to time the Ministry of Labour (MOL) issues, discontinues, amends or re-issues labour and immigration laws, which as mentioned apply to employers operating in the UAE. As an employer, you should therefore ensure you check contracts with a lawyer versed in UAE employment laws.

Basic Information

The employment contract should be explicit, easy to understand and written in line with the UAE Labour Law. It should include:

- A statement that this is an employment contract between the company and the employee
- Joining date, defined as the date the employee commences his/her duty on completion of all necessary joining formalities
- Period of employment in respect to limited (fixed-term) or unlimited (open-ended) contracts, in accordance with the UAE Labour Law. The terms and conditions must be clearly stated along with the type of contract
- Probation period which could be between three to six months. However, the maximum period must be six months in line with the UAE Labour Law. This clause should include a brief statement of performance requirements, formal assessment during this period, conditions for termination and applicable notice period (as applicable)
- Relocation/transfer details (if an internal appointment) with all associated costs. These should be discussed and agreed by both parties and be borne by the employer

Responsibilities

The employment contract should detail duties and responsibilities of the role, including:

- The job title and grade/level of the employee, as applicable
- Department
- Working conditions
- Working hours
- Nature of the work he/she will carry out
- Place of work
- Overtime requirements if any, with payment as per UAE law and time of payment specified

GOING THROUGH A THOROUGH SET OF CHECKS BEFORE ENGAGING A NEW EMPLOYEE IS LIKELY TO SAVE A COMPANY ANY UNWELCOME SURPRISES FURTHER DOWN THE LINE

Remuneration Package

Compensation and benefits should include, as per employer policy:

- Basic salary
- Allowances, e.g. housing or transportation, as per company policy, job grade or level
- Increment and bonus schemes, performance-based and subject to the employer's discretion
- Annual leave period stating any applicable conditions, such as leave during probation
- Leave ticket, whether for self, or self and eligible dependents
- Medical, life and accident insurance (see Health & Safety)
- Sponsorship of residence for the employee stating applicable terms and conditions. For example the company may assist in processing family visas where practical and possible, however the fees for this would normally be borne by the employee

And as per UAE Labour Law:

- Employee's compensation covering accidents at work
- Sick leave
- Maternity leave for female employees
- Al Uddah leave for Muslim employees
- End of service benefits for non-UAE nationals
- Government pension scheme for UAE nationals with valid ID card (Khulasat Al Qaid)

Employer Protection

When completing an employment contract, certain scenarios should be considered by any employer:

- Retirement age is normally 60 years as per the UAE Labour Law. Any extension is at the discretion of the employer
- The employee engaging in any outside activity related to his/her job functions or business activities for payment or profit or that which impacts his/her primary duties with the employer. Applicable conditions can be included within the contract
- The employee should declare that he/she does not have any obligations to a prior employer or third party which would restrict his/her ability to carry out company related duties. A brief statement should be included that any restrictions arising due to any confidential obligations under the previous employment will have been disclosed to the employer
- Intellectual property rights, in terms of their definition, terms and conditions that the employee will agree to
- Confidentiality aspects, in terms of their definition, terms and

AN EMPLOYMENT CONTRACT CAN BE TERMINATED IF BOTH PARTIES AGREE, PROVIDED THAT THE EMPLOYEE'S WRITTEN CONSENT IS GIVEN

conditions that the employee will agree to

- Any advanced loans or payments made to the employee which may be duly deducted from the final settlement or end of service dues
- Changes in domestic circumstances. In this case the employee should advise his/her employer in writing. The employer will then revise the employment terms as applicable. A married person's contract, or employees with children, may allow for an additional level of accommodation allowance, air ticket provision, school fees or health insurance benefits, for example

Restrictive Covenant Clause

It may be that as an employee, to protect your own competitive interests following the termination of employment on either side, that the contract states the employee will refrain from either directly or indirectly soliciting or attempting to solicit the business of any client or customer of the employer within the UAE. Similarly, that the employee will refrain from withdrawing any other staff member under your employ.

As an employer you might also decide, within the initial contract, to include a ban preventing the employee working for a direct competitor within the UAE for a limited period of time on leaving the company.

ARABIC TRANSLATION

Many documents and contracts will need to be translated to Arabic and there are many language companies available to undertake this work, including revin.ae, industryarabic.com, and transperfect.com.

Termination

An employment contract can be terminated if both parties agree, provided that the employee's written consent is given; the employer must then cancel the employee's residence visa and labour card. Employees are free to switch jobs anywhere in the UAE once they have completed the minimum two or three years' service as per their contract.

If an employee is in breach of their contract, violates the UAE Labour Law, or absconds, you can apply to the Ministry of Labour for a labour ban to be placed on their file. Then, if they apply for a new job, their application for a labour card would be rejected.

CREDIT: *This section has been written with the professional advice of Shailaja Khan, senior associate consultant with Dubai-based HR consulting firm, Kompass Consultancy (kompassconsultancy.com).*

EMPLOYEE GUIDELINES
FOR EMPLOYMENT CONTRACTS

Before accepting an employment contract, a prospective employee should ask themselves:

- Are the key tasks and accountabilities of the role clear? Do the role's requirements and working conditions meet expectations?
- Are the compensation and benefits in line with market standards and commensurate to the role in question?
- Are there any additional benefits such as education allowance, furniture allowance, provisions for compassionate leave, or study leave that should be considered or requested if not included?
- What is the scope of medical coverage and does this satisfactorily cover personal circumstances?
- Is there scope for career development or opportunity for growth in line with individual career aspirations?
- How much travel will the role require? Is this local, regional or international? Is this compensated?
- Is the culture of the organisation and its work environment a comfortable fit?
- Is the structure of the organisation/department clarified?
- Is there clarity with regard to employment recognition schemes?
- Have you completed all necessary due diligence on the new employer?

When negotiating any aspects of a new employment contract, consider:

- The start date – ensure it is realistic and will give you an opportunity to leave your previous role ready to start your new role with optimum energy and focus
- Salary and bonus scheme – check this is competitive within the market and commensurate with your job role
- Car allowance and any associated travelling costs
- Pre-planned leave during the probation period

ONLINE CHECKS

Employees can check their contract and view their e-labour card through the eNetwasal service at the Ministry of Labour's website, mol.gov.ae. These can be viewed just 48 hours after an employer applies to the MOL.

UAE LABOUR LAW

The UAE Labour Law outlines information on employee entitlements, employment contracts and disciplinary rules. The law is employer friendly, but it also clearly outlines employee rights. You can download a copy of the document from the Ministry of Labour website (mol.gov. ae); the document has not been fully updated for some time so it's worth keeping an eye on the website as new laws are in progress.

If you're setting up a business and planning on employing staff then it's essential to get up to speed and stay up-to-date on UAE Labour Law. While there are similarities with elsewhere in the world, it's crucial to make note of some of the specific procedures applicable here.

The UAE Labour Law is primarily set up to protect the interests of employees. It outlines aspects such as employee entitlements, contracts, disciplinary rules and the mandatory requirements employers are obliged to meet in terms of, for example, working hours or health and safety provision.

The labour law is extensive in its coverage of employment matters, and while new revisions are issued infrequently, you can download a copy from the Ministry of Labour website, mol.gov.ae.

As Alexander McGeogh, senior legal consultant at law firm Hadef & Partners points out, the UAE Labour Law lays down the rules that apply throughout the private sector (except Dubai International Financial Centre which we discuss later).

General Laws

Employment Contracts
Once you have offered somebody a job you will be need them to sign an employment contract; this should list the starting date, type of employment, location, terms and conditions, duration and the salary. This is a legally binding agreement that should be written in both Arabic and English. You must register the labour contract and card of employees online at mol.gov.ae. An employee can terminate their employment contract if both parties agree, provided that your written consent is given; you will then need to cancel the employee's residence visa.

Probation
Probation periods can be set for a maximum of six months. Some companies delay the residency process until the probation period is up, which can make settling in difficult for employees – no residency means they can't sponsor family members, buy a car or get a bank loan.

By law, employees are not entitled to paid sick leave during probation and most firms do not grant paid annual leave to be taken during this time. Annual leave will still be accrued through that, which the employee can take over the course of the year.

Leave

While on sick leave, the employee is entitled to the first 15 days with full pay, the next 30 days are with half pay, and any subsequent days are unpaid. Annual holiday starts at one calendar month per year, roughly 22 working days.

Working Hours

As Friday is the Islamic holy day, working weeks run from Sunday to Thursday; Friday and Saturday being the weekend. Some companies only take off the Friday; others have a five and a half day week. Working hours differ dramatically between companies; straight shifts vary from 7am to 2.30pm for government organisations to the common 9am to 6pm for private companies. Most retail outlets tend to open from 10am to 10pm but often operate shifts. A break for food, rest or prayer is required after every five hours of continuous work.

The maximum number of hours permitted per week is 48, although some industries, such as hospitality and retail, have longer stipulated hours. Public holidays are set by the government, while the timing of religious holidays depends on the sighting of the moon. This means that it can be difficult to plan holidays as confirmation of time off may be announced as late as the day before. All employees are entitled to a shorter working day during Ramadan, typically two hours less.

Gratuity Payments

An employee on a fixed-term contract, who has completed one or more years of continuous service, will be entitled to 21 days' pay for each of the first five years of service, and 30 days' pay for each additional year as an end-of-service gratuity payment; this compensates for the lack of a pension system. This is based on their basic salary (not including basic housing, transport and utilities). The total end of service gratuity should not exceed the salary of two years. Leaving before the end of a fixed-term contract or being fired for breaking UAE Labour Law could result in the loss of their gratuity payment.

Key Employment Issues

There are certain areas of the law concerning employment that all employers should be aware of. If you're starting a business and plan on having staff, then the following areas may be applicable at various points during your operation.

THE MAXIMUM NUMBER OF HOURS PERMITTED PER WEEK IS 48, ALTHOUGH SOME INDUSTRIES, SUCH AS HOSPITALITY AND RETAIL, HAVE LONGER STIPULATED HOURS

Employees Moving Jobs

Officially, as an employer in the private sector, you can ban any employee from working in the UAE for up to six months should they leave before the end of their contracted term. In a free zone, this may be restricted to only a work ban within that same free zone. In reality, rather than trying to enforce a ban through the Ministry of Labour, most employers are happy to supply a no objection certificate (NOC) and let the employee take up employment elsewhere. This ban is also not applicable to certain professions such as teachers, engineers and doctors.

To cover yourself, though, it may be worth adding a non-compete clause in employment contracts. This will give you official grounds to stop an employee going to a direct competitor if you feel that is something that could be detrimental to your business.

If an employee has completed their contract period, either two or three years, they can legally move jobs without needing an NOC from you. There are some exceptions to when your employees can transfer their sponsor without your approval, such as your death, a change of in the ownership of your company, your company closing and the cancellation of your company's trade licence.

MINISTRY OF LABOUR

There are various leaflets and publications from the Ministry of Labour that explain the different aspects of UAE labour law. Find out more at mol.gov.ae, where you can select downloadable resources. To speak to a representative, call 800 665.

Employees Absconding

Anyone leaving the country or their job permanently without informing their employer and cancelling the residence visa with their sponsor will be classed as 'absconding' and may receive a ban; as an employer though, you'll have to wait six months to report absconders who have left the country. If they remain in the country, that period is reduced to seven days. Absconders should be reported to the Ministry of Labour, who then pass information on to the GDRFA and the relevant police force to the emirate you're in.

If a potential employee is banned, their computer file will show it during the application for their residence visa and labour card and the application will be rejected. Also, if an employee leaves the country or are unaccountable for seven days in a row or 20 days in total, your can terminate their employment contract without awarding any gratuity pay or any outstanding benefits.

Redundancy

If you need to make an employee redundant, there are things you can do to make the process less painful for them. For starters, giving them a few months leeway so they can find another employer, rather than the standard 30 days they'll get as soon as you cancel their visa, is likely to be very beneficial. This is something that the UAE Labour Law condones.

If you're taking over a company, or selling your business, or you're changing the structure of your business, then the employee's employment contract remains valid for six months after the changeover. Only after that six months can you or the new business owner cancel those contracts.

Terminating A Contract

Employers are protected by the law should they need to terminate an employee's contract without notice and with immediate effect. The following can all be legitimate reasons for doing so:

- If the employee has submitted fake documents or assumed a nationality other than their own
- At any point during the probation period
- If a mistake by the employee is responsible for a substantial financial loss to the company, so long as the Ministry of Labour is told about it within 48 hours
- If the employee breaks health and safety regulations. However, these need to have been displayed in a permanent place, or given orally if the employee is illiterate
- If the employee fails to carry out basic contractual duties. This involves an initial written warning with termination should they subsequently continue to not perform
- If the employee discloses a secret of your establishment
- If the employee is convicted of a crime involving honour, honesty and public morals
- If the employee is drunk or intoxicated by drugs during work hours
- If the employee physically assaults a colleague, manager or employer during work
- If they are absent for without legitimate reason for 20 intermittent days or more than seven continuous days in a year

Conversely, the employee can terminate their contract immediately should your company not meet its side of the contract agreement. This can include instances such as not paying wages on time, or if you as the employer, or your legal representative, assaults them.

Courts

For mainland companies, any claim an employee has against a company must first be brought to the Ministry of Labour (MOL). If no quick agreement can be reached, the MOL issues a court referral letter. Each emirate has its own court, hence the emirate in which the company's trade licence is issued deals with the case within its own court system.

For free zones the system is different in that most have their own labour dispute sections, although any court action would then be referred to the federal court system. The exception to this is Dubai International Financial Centre (DIFC), which runs its own courts, under the DIFC Judicial Authority.

The main elements of the DIFC justice system are the Court of First Instance, which handles the larger cases, and the Small Claims Tribunal. The DIFC Court of First Instance bears all the formalities you might expect from a UK court process, for example. There are no limits on the claim value and the limitation for commencing a claim is within six years of right of action. Fees are 5% of the claim value, to a minimum of US$1,000 and maximum of US$20,000.

Cases at the DIFC Small Claims Tribunal are generally heard within a couple of months. It has jurisdiction over claims that do not exceed Dhs.100,000 (regardless of subject matter) or Dhs.200,000 in the case of an employment claim (it can be in excess of this as long as both parties agree). However, as the rules stand now, neither party is allowed to be legally represented. Issue fees are 2% of the claim value, to a minimum of US$55 and maximum of US$4000.

UAE Corporate Law Firms

Al Hanaee 04 3809666, *alhanaee.com*
Al Tamimi & Company 02 813 0444, *tamimi.com*
Baker & Mackenzie 02 846 1888, *bakernet.com*
Clyde & Co 02 644 6633, *clydeco.com*
Davidson & Co 04 343 8897, *davidson-legal.com*
Fichte & Company Legal Consultancy 04 435 7577, *fichtelegal.com*
Galadari Associates & Legal Consultants 04 393 7700, *galadarilaw.com*
Hadef & Partners 04 429 2999, *hadefpartners.com*
Trowers & Hamlins 04 3519201, *trowers.com*

CREDIT: *The DIFC section was written with the advice of Jamie Liddington, senior associate, Hadef & Partners.*

FOR MAINLAND COMPANIES, ANY CLAIM AN EMPLOYEE HAS AGAINST A COMPANY MUST FIRST BE BROUGHT TO THE MINISTRY OF LABOUR

HEALTH & SAFETY

Part C of the UAE's Employment Law Guide details occupational health and safety. This is extremely extensive to discuss in full, but Hadef & Partners outlines some of the main aspects here.

Employers are obliged to maintain healthy working conditions, be it within an industrial, office, retail or other work environment. This ranges from environments that are dangerous, those that might contain noxious fumes or unsuitable heat conditions, through to having the correct levels of lighting, fully-maintained first aid boxes, serviceable fire extinguishers and robust health and safety processes. 'Remote' sites need to meet minimum accommodation and recreational facilities standards, have adequate transporation provision, first aid facilities, and also suitable food and water supplies.

In practice, ministry inspectors can and do conduct on-the-spot inspections of any work site. This is not only in terms of checking working conditions, but any other aspect of the labour law such as sponsorship and visa compliance, remuneration and other factors. These visits may be triggered by suspected infringements, or even on an ad-hoc basis.

For industrial sites, the health and safety requirements extend to all the relevant aspects of providing full personal protective equipment, safe working precautions, underground work and electrical hazards. During the UAE's gruelling summer months, employers are also required to provide labourers with a four-hour rest period in the middle of the day (between 12pm and 4pm) with adequate shade.

In the case of injury, death or disablement, employers are obliged to report the incident in full to the authorities, provide adequate compensation to the employee's dependents and pay for medical treatment as required in the situation. Each is clearly shown in sections C5 and C6 of the Employment Law Guide. If working hours are deemed as particularly dangerous, employers are obliged to reduce these from eight to seven.

Health Insurance Laws

A significant clause within the UAE Labour Law is that all employers have a duty to provide medical care for their employees. Each of the seven emirates has its own health insurance laws, some more established than others.

For example, in recent years Abu Dhabi has made it mandatory for both public and private sector firms to provide health insurance to all employees and has a list of government-approved insurers that companies can select from. In Dubai, public sector companies have the same obligation, and a law for the private sector is being implemented.

Dubai is swiftly being brought into line with the capital's law following the Health Insurance Law No 11 of 2013 which will make it mandatory for employers to provide medical insurance for all employees. There are three staging dates for compliance with this law. Large employers (1,000+ employees) have to comply by 1 November 2014. Employers with 100-999 employees need to comply by end of July 2015 and all other employers (including those employing domestic staff) must comply by the end of June 2016.

Residence visas will not be granted unless the applicant has valid health insurance. Employers won't be able to avoid these costs for employees, and those who are found not to comply are likely to be given a fine of between Dhs.500 and Dhs.150,000. This can increase up to Dhs.500,000 where there are repeated offences.

Health & Safety Training

GEMS Quality Consultants 04 251 2560, *gemsqc.com*
Numero Uno 02 557 5220, *numerouno-me.com*
RRC Middle East Dubai 04 354 7473, *rrc.co.ae*
Safety World M.E. Consultants 04 358 2131, *safety-world.net*
Safe Way Security and Safety Consultancy 050 2112 471, *safewaysafety.com*

Medical Insurance

Abu Dhabi National Insurance Company 800 8040, *adnic.ae*
Aetna Global 438 7500, *aetnainternational.com*
Al Salam Insurance 254 9666, *alsalamins.com*
AXA Insurance 800 4845, *axa-gulf.com*
Dubai Islamic Insurance & Reinsurance Co 800 4998, *aman-diir.ae*
Greenshield Insurance Brokers 388 2200, *greenshield.ae*
Lifecare 331 8688, *lifecareinternational.com*
Nexus Insurance 323 1111, *nexusadvice.com*
Noor Takaful Insurance 800 6667, *noortakaful.com*
Oman Insurance Company 800 4746, *tameen.ae*
Orient Insurance 253 1300, *insuranceuae.com*
Salama Islamic Arab Insurance 800 725 262, *salama.ae*
Union Insurance 800 84248, *unioninsuranceuae.com*

CREDIT: *Hadef & Partners (hadefpartners.com)*

A SIGNIFICANT CLAUSE WITHIN THE UAE LABOUR LAW IS THAT ALL EMPLOYERS HAVE A DUTY TO PROVIDE MEDICAL CARE FOR THEIR EMPLOYEES

"WHAT STARTED IN DUBAI CAN NOW BE FOUND ON A GLOBAL LEVEL"

Delice is a premium gourmet and chocolatier established in Dubai in 2004. Specialising in premium quality Mediterranean sweets, Delice's unique products are handcrafted by a team of connoisseurs. Having started with Dhs.100,000, the business now earns a multimillion dollar net profit.

Jalel Ghayaza
Business Founder, Delice
Web Delice-Dubai.com
Activities Gourmet confectioner
Strengths Creativity, PR, sales, marketing

What made you decide to set up your business in the UAE?
Dubai has always been a hub for all businesses serving many countries worldwide. Most importantly, there is high security in the UAE. The working and living conditions are perfect, and it feels like a second home.

Additionally, the luxury market is extremely important in the region, but I saw that it all came from abroad. I realised that there was a gap in the market for luxury confectionery; not only in terms of the quality of the product, but in terms of its presentation. I realised that I could explore this field, and bring innovation to it. Furthermore, the country is a meeting point for east and west. I devised the concept of creating a product that had the best of both worlds: the richness and diversity of traditional Mediterranean sweets, enhanced with the finesse of European technique.

Any Advice?
Be a good listener; don't assume you've entered the business world knowing everything. You should talk little and listen to everything with a great deal of attention. Also, really take time to meditate about the risks and rewards of every decision you make.

We also brought a whole new, revolutionary image to products that were considered so simple before, such as dates, and we are the only chocolatiers in the world who sell chocolate boxes with 24K gold plating. Finally, we complement our product with excellent service standards.

What challenges did you face in setting up in the UAE?
The biggest challenge was starting with Dhs.100,000. We had to keep the company alive for at least the first eight months, until we got our first contract with Madinat Jumeirah. We then had to produce 12,000 boxes of welcome room amenities a month, but at the time I only had four employees. I had to raise that number to 18 within 72 hours. Going ahead of our competitors was

important as well, and that could only be achieved by offering an outstandingly original product, with tasteful and diverse packaging, complemented by excellent customer service.

How does the reality differ from expectations?
It is a big responsibility, especially when the initial resources to start the business were very limited. Success was not guaranteed, but a combination of learning from previous mistakes, working hard and for long hours, and being creative and patient, are elements that contributed to success.

How has Delice grown since you started the company?
I started with a Dhs.100,000 bank loan. Currently, Delice averages sales of over US$10 million, and this figure is still going up. Delice has expanded not only in terms of brand value, but it is getting to the global level; what started in Dubai can now be found in exclusive locations in London, Yerevan, Bahrain and, soon, Saudi Arabia. While our global expansion will most likely continue, we are determined to keep Dubai as the production centre in order to guarantee the same quality standards.

How do you switch off from the constant pressure?
I usually highly enjoy the pressure. I actually do not consider it pressure as I enjoy the long hours at work. Spending time with my family after work is the most relaxing time I could have.

What is the most rewarding thing about seeing your idea turn into reality?
It was a hard fight for 10 years, and I do not recall having a single day off throughout the first six of them. I still spend a great deal of time in my business, but I do it from a different, possibly more comfortable position. It's hugely rewarding to see that my product has been warmly welcomed by so many people, both in the UAE and the rest of the world. It's giving them an experience to cherish, in just one bite.

What advice would you give to other entrepreneurs setting up in the UAE?
Be strong in terms of capital: have an extremely conservative business plan and make sure you have enough funds to cover the expenses of the business for at least the first two years. Also, care for your employees and suppliers just as much as you would for your clients. In the end, they are your most important partners, and the execution of your product lies upon them. Make them feel like working at your company is a pleasure – where they are respected as human beings, and where every day is a learning experience and not a burden.

CARE FOR YOUR EMPLOYEES AND SUPPLIERS JUST AS MUCH AS YOU WOULD FOR YOUR CLIENTS. IN THE END, THEY ARE YOUR MOST IMPORTANT PARTNERS, AND THE EXECUTION OF YOUR PRODUCT LIES UPON THEM

OFFICE
MANAGEMENT

THE UAE HAS A HUGE NUMBER OF SUPPLIERS FOR ALL OFFICE NEEDS, FROM THE MOST BASIC TO THE DELUXE AND EVERYTHING IN BETWEEN

IN THE UAE IT IS POLITE BUSINESS ETIQUETTE TO READ A CONTACT'S BUSINESS CARD WHEN IT IS GIVEN TO YOU

BUSINESSES SET UP IN A FREE ZONE CANNOT TRADE WITH CUSTOMERS ONSHORE

To help you get your business off the ground you will need to purchase essential tools and equipment, so do account for these start-up costs. The UAE has a huge number of suppliers for all office needs, from the most basic to the deluxe and everything in between.

Sourcing suppliers and negotiating deals and contracts for products will be a large aspect of setting up a new business, but the directory below will save you hours of searching the web. Here's a checklist to get you started:

Furniture & Decor

Abanos Furniture & Decoration Industry 04 885 1885, *abanos.ae*
ACE Hardware 06 537 1556, *aceuae.com*
Alexandria International Furniture 06 534 3633, *alexandriaintl.com*
BAFCO 04 3350045, *bafco.com*
Casa Nova 04 338 6180, *casanovadubai.com*
E-Walls 04 399 4748, *ewalls-s.com*
ID Design 02 443 7557, *iddesignuae.com*
IKEA 800 IKEA, *ikeauae.com*
The Living Zone 04 341 1220, *thelivingzone.ae*
Mahmayi Office Furniture 04 221 2358, *mahmayiofficefurniture.com*
Marlin Furniture 800 MARLIN, *marlinfurniture.com*
Naser Al Sayer & Co 06 574 9030, *nasco-uae.com*
Pan Emirates Home Furnishings 04 383 0800, *panemirates.com*
Rigid Industries 06 557 0701, *rigidfze.com*
SAGTCO 04 457 2779, *sagtco.com*
United Office Systems 04 337 0131, *unitedofficesys.com*

OFFICE FURNITURE AND EQUIPMENT

- Desks
- File cabinets
- Overhead and work lighting
- Client seating
- Fireproof safe
- Paper shredder
- Photocopier
- Alarm system
- Fire extinguisher
- First-aid kit

- Computer hardware, accessories and software
- Communications
- Telephone line
- Internet connection
- Fax machine
- Answering machine/service
- General office supplies
- Business cards
- Stationery

Stationery

Al Gurg Stationery 04 225 2531, *algurgstationery.com*
Altimus 04 396 7730, *altimus.ae*
Emirates Trading 04 337 5050, *go-etrading.com*
Farook International Stationery 04 352 1997, *farook.com*
Modern Stationery 04 336 9975, *modestoffice.com*
Objects & Elements 04 323 6182, *objectsandelementsgroup.com*
Office Store 04 351 8117, *officestoreuae.com*
Office Works 04 368 9400, *officeworksme.com*
Prints Design 04 344 7964, *printsdesign.ae*
Quick Office 04 452 2261, *quickoffice.ae*
Simple Office 04 320 7940, *simpleoffice.ae*

Technology

Inditech 04 398 0781, *inditechics.com*
Information Technology Services 04 343 4123, *its-dxb.ae*
Key Information Technology 04 340 0666, *kit.ae*
MDS UAE 02 627 6354, *mds.ae*
Spectrum Information Technology Services 04 443 8165, *spectrum-its.com*
Unicorp 02 449 9094, *unicorptechnology.ae*

Water Delivery

Al Bayan Water 800 4223, *albayanwateruae.com*
Al Shalal Water 800 4342, *alshalalwaters.com*
Aqua Water 04 339 3028, *aquauae.com*
Culligan International 800 4945, *culligan.com*
Falcon Spring Drinking Water 04 396 6072, *falconspringwater.com*
Masafi 600 5455, *masafi.com*
Nestle Waters Management & Technology 04 324 0800, *nestle-waters.com*
Oasis Water 600 522 261, *oasiscome2life.com*
Voss Water 04 884 8811, *vosswater.com*

Postal & Courier

Aramex 600 544 000, *aramex.com*
DHL Express 800 4004, *dhl.co.ae*
Emirates Post 600 599 999, *emiratespostuae.com*
Empost 600 565 555, *empostuae.com*
Fastrack 04 266 6610, *ftcourier.net*
Federal Express 800 FED EX, *fedex.com*
Skycom Express 600 532 224, *skycomex.com*
Sky Express International 04 268 0654, *skyexpress.ae*

Cleaning Services

Al Tanmyah Services 04 298 0051, *tanmyah.ae*
Beauty World 04 360 5058, *360-cleaning.com*

Focus Maids 04 380 6222, *focusmaids.net*
Liverpool Cleaning Services 800 2532 6464,
liverpooldubai.com
Morning Star 02 677 4274, *morningstar-uae.com*
Oriental 04 265 5444, *ocs.ae*
Smart Touch 04 338 3744, *smartcleaningdubai.com*

Maintenance

Dubai Technical 050 9113 683, *dubaitechnical.com*
Hitches & Glitches 800 42634,
hitchesandglitches.com
Jim Will Fix It 800 349, *jimwillfixitservices.com*
Toolman 800 3312, *toolman.ae*
Yes We Fix 800 993, *yeswefix.ae*

INFO

MARKETING

Without customers, your business, big or small, would not survive. To attract and retain customers, you will need a marketing plan that helps your customers understand why your product or service is better than, or different from, the competition. Developing a marketing plan requires research, time and commitment, but there is a wide choice of marketing companies in the UAE to help you reach your target audience, boost your customer base, and ultimately, increase your bottom line.

MARKETING & PR COMPANIES

Several companies also offer branding, design and advertising services as well as traditional marketing and PR.
Blue Apple Mediacom 04 439 0161,
blueapplemediacom.com
DNA Communication 04 392 2490, *dnacomm.com*
DPQ 04 3489475, *dpq.ae*
Iris Public Relation 04 434 1207, *irispr.net*
Katch International 04 3468353, *katchinternational.com*
McCollins Media 04 445 6848, *mccollinsmedia.com*
Origin Communications Group 04 367 2270,
grouporigin.com
The Public Relations Company 050 7681 684, *tprc.ae*
Sahara Communications 04 329 8996, *saharagcc.com*
Sept PR 04 4538280, *septpr.com*
TishTash *tishtash.com*
TOH PR 04 3549212, *tohpr.com*

DOING BUSINESS

BUSINESS
TRAVELLERS

THE UAE HAS WORKED HARD TO STRATEGICALLY LEVERAGE ITS ADVANTAGEOUS LOCATION AND MODERN INFRASTRUCTURE FOR BUSINESS TRAVELLERS AND INDUSTRY ALIKE

DUBAI PICKS UP

50%

OF THE MIDDLE EAST'S MICE BUSINESS

DUBAI'S EXPO 2020 IS PREDICTED TO CREATE 277,000 JOBS

Situated at the heart of a powerful trade road running from the Middle East through to Africa, India and wider Asia, the UAE – and Dubai in particular – has reaped the benefits of a global emerging markets resurgence, building fast and furiously to meet the needs of a growing international business community.

The now-gleaming metropolis of Dubai boasts 'business' as its middle name. The emirate's modern-day success is carved from its early heritage as a trade hub, and today the city remains a major facilitator of trade and re-exporter of goods and services.

As a whole, the UAE has worked hard to strategically leverage its advantageous location and modern infrastructure for business travellers and industry alike. With ambitious transport projects either completed or near completion, such as the Dubai Metro and nationwide airport and rail expansions, it is now easier than ever to do business in the country.

Dubai holds the enviable position of picking up around 50% of the Middle East's total MICE business. The corporate-friendly emirate welcomed 10 million visitors to its 599 hotels in 2013, and around 20% of those were business-related.

Abu Dhabi received 2.8 million guests in 2013 across 131 hotels. Business tourism currently accounts for approximately 70% of the capital emirate's hotel guest profile, with 10% of this emanating from the MICE segment. Both emirates are heavily targeting the MICE sector going forward.

In what will be the UAE's biggest test to date for its business traveller capacity, Dubai won the bid to host the World Expo 2020, the world's largest trade show, to be held under the theme Connecting minds, Creating the future.

Dubai's upcoming 438-hectare site is set to be one of the largest and glitziest Expo locations ever developed, equidistant from the centres of Abu Dhabi and Dubai, next to Al Maktoum International Airport and in close proximity to Jebel Ali Port.

It is already predicted that there will be an influx to the region of 25 million visitors. The knock-on effect is a predicted 277,000 jobs created for the region and a huge boost for Dubai's infrastructure.

DUBAI WELCOMED 10 MILLION VISITORS TO ITS 599 HOTELS IN 2013, AND AROUND 20% OF THOSE WERE BUSINESS-RELATED

Visa Regulations

Everyone entering the UAE needs a visit visa, except for citizens of GCC countries; this must then be transferred to a residence visa if you plan to live and work here. The procedures vary depending on your nationality (see How To... No.18). Always check the regulations before travelling as details can change.

18

HOW TO...

APPLY FOR A VISIT VISA

The procedure for obtaining a UAE visit visa depends on your nationality. GCC citizens do not require a visa, while nationalities from 33 other countries (see list at left) will obtain a 30-day visa on arrival. All other nationalities must apply for a visit visa in advance – this needs to be sponsored by a hotel or tour operator, or by a UAE resident.

VISA ON ARRIVAL

Citizens of the following countries receive an automatic visit visa on arrival: Andorra, Australia, Austria, Belgium, Brunei, Canada, Denmark, Finland, France, Germany, Greece, Hong Kong, Iceland, Ireland, Italy, Japan, Liechtenstein, Luxembourg, Malaysia, Monaco, Netherlands, New Zealand, Norway, Portugal, San Marino, Singapore, South Korea, Spain, Sweden, Switzerland, UK, US and Vatican City.

If the latter, the visit visa can be applied for by either an individual or corporate sponsor, allowing the visitor to stay in the UAE for a short-term (30 days) or long-term (90 days) stay. It is usually issued to those who are on a business trip, plan to stay with a friend or relative, or those who have planned a holiday. The visit visa permits one entry into the UAE within two months of the date of issue.

PREREQUISITES

• A family member can sponsor a visitor if he/she is resident in the UAE. His or her monthly salary must be a minimum of Dhs.4,000 (or Dhs.3,000 plus accommodation)
• A GCC resident can sponsor a visitor as long as he or she is a business person, company manager or representative, or holds a professional post
• A GCC resident can sponsor his wife as long as she has a valid residence visa in her husband's GCC country and he resides in the UAE
• Tourist visas (valid for 30, 40, or 60 days) can only be applied for through a licensed hotel, travel or tourism agency. See visaprocess.ae for further information
• Minimum six months validity on passport

WHAT TO BRING

• Visitor's passport (copy)
• One passport-sized photo of the sponsored person
• Fees: Dhs.620 for a 30-day visa or Dhs.1,120 for a 90-day visa; additional Dhs.100 for urgent processing (optional); Dhs.1,000 refundable deposit
• Two application forms typed in English or Arabic (downloaded from dnrd.gov.ae)
• A letter stating the reason and purpose of the visit (proof of relationship may be required)

COMPANY SPONSORS MUST PROVIDE:
• Trade licence (copy)
• Establishment immigration card
• Representative card (original and copy)
• Profession of the visitor in relation to the GDRFA codes (see dnrd.gov.ae)

INDIVIDUAL SPONSORS MUST PROVIDE:
• Two application forms in English and Arabic (typed)
• Sponsor's employment contract (original and copy) to be attested by the GDRFA on payment (costs Dhs.130)
• Sponsor's salary certificate (dated within the last three months)
• Sponsor's municipality-attested tenancy contract (copy) – unless accommodation is provided by employer
• Attested marriage certificate if sponsoring spouse (from UAE embassy in home country and Ministry of Foreign Affairs in UAE)
• Attested birth certificate of child (from UAE embassy in home country and Ministry of Foreign Affairs in UAE)

PROCEDURE

WHERE: General Directorate of Residency and Foreigners Affairs (GDRFA)
• Sponsor visits a typing centre with documents to complete the application form and pay the fees
• Sponsor submits documents to the visa section of the GDRFA
• Pay the visa deposit fee at the bank counter
• Collect the visa
• Visa is faxed or emailed to the visitor; sponsor keeps a copy
• Sponsor collects the original visa at the visa counter in the airport (next to the arrivals hall) at least two hours before visitor arrives, and has the copy stamped
• Once the visitor lands in the UAE, exchange copy of the visa for the original at the immigration desk in the airport
• Passport is stamped at passport control in the airport
• All visitors who need to apply for a visit visa before arrival must have an eye scan (retina scan) at passport control
• The Dhs.1,000 deposit is refunded once you leave the UAE
• For an additional Dhs.200, a multiple-entry visa holder is eligible to use the airport e-Gates.

OVERSTAYING

if you remain in the UAE beyond your permitted period of stay, you will have to pay a fine of Dhs.100, plus Dhs.100 for each day you have overstayed. This fine must be paid before you are permitted to leave.

GETTING HERE & AROUND

The UAE is geared up for cars, and has a good and continuously improving infrastructure. There are some good public transport options but most people travel by car, whether that's driving themselves, using the generally excellent and inexpensive taxi service, or hiring a private driver.

Car Hire

To hire any vehicle you will need to provide a passport copy, credit card and a valid driving licence a small economy car should cost you around Dhs.1,700-2,000 per month, but it's worth shopping around to get the best deal. Most leasing companies include the following in their rates: registration, maintenance, replacement, 24 hour assistance and insurance.

Public Transport

The UAE's public transport is improving rapidly, particularly in Dubai where you can travel by metro, water taxi, and on the new Dubai Tram (running from Marsa Dubai to the Burj Al Arab). There are bus systems in all emirates, and taxis are practically everywhere. In Dubai, Nol cards are used to pay for public transport and street car parking. They are rechargeable and can

Dubai Metro

be used on the metro, bus, and water buses, with fares calculated depending on how many zones your journey takes you through.

In Abu Dhabi, the Orja card is used on all bus services.

Dubai Metro
The metro is the centrepiece of Dubai's efforts and, since its opening in September 2009, has helped to reduce the overall number of daily drivers. The metro runs the length of the city stopping at major landmarks, and trains are regular and fast.

Bus
Buses run within and between all emirates at very affordable rates. Dubai's bus system, along with other parts of the country, has also seen major improvements over the past few years with the introduction of air-conditioned bus stops, new buses and an increase in routes. The RTA's fleet of water buses offers commuters and travellers an expanding network of routes along Dubai's waterways; alternatively, there is a more costly water taxi service – operating from Deira across to Jebel Ali.

Taxis
If you don't have a car, taxis are still the most common way of getting around. Call 04 208 0808 to book a taxi in Dubai, or 600 5353 53 in Abu Dhabi.

The Hala Taxi fleet is the newest fleet in Dubai. You can't flag them down as they only respond to telephone or online bookings. The cars are black or white, and equipped with wi-fi, Nol and NFC payment systems (for smartphones).

Flights
The UAE is well placed to reach destinations in Africa, Asia and Europe. In fact, 100 capital cities are within a six-hour flight from Abu Dhabi and Dubai. Most European capitals and major cities have direct flights to Abu Dhabi International Airport (code: AUH) or Dubai International Airport (DXB), with Etihad Airways and Emirates, the national airlines of the UAE.

Dubai International Airport's three terminals are a 15 to 30 minute taxi ride apart, depending on the traffic, and there's also a shuttle bus. Most of the better-known airlines use Terminal 1, while Terminal 2 is used primarily by flydubai and airlines serving former Soviet countries and central Asia. Terminal 3, which opened in 2008, is the newest and most luxurious of the three and exclusively dedicated to Emirates

100 CAPITAL CITIES ARE WITHIN A SIX-HOUR FLIGHT FROM ABU DHABI AND DUBAI. MOST EUROPEAN CAPITALS AND MAJOR CITIES HAVE DIRECT FLIGHTS

Airline. The Dubai World Central Al Maktoum International Airport, which is located closer to Abu Dhabi – near the Jebel Ali Free Zone and Jebel Ali Port – opened in late 2013. All terminals offer car rental, hotel reservations and exchange services. Etihad runs its own private bus service, which is free for those with a boarding pass and makes the journey between Abu Dhabi International Airport and Dubai.

Royal Jet is an international luxury flight operator based in Abu Dhabi, with a fleet of private charter planes, including a Boeing Business Jet for VIPs with ostrich skin covered seatbacks and luxury beds. On Abu Dhabi island you'll also find Al Bateen Executive Airport (code: OMAD), which focuses on private jets.

Al Ain airport flies to nine destinations and is served by seven airlines, and there are also airports in Sharjah, Fujairah and Ras Al Khaimah.

Airlines
Currently, over 100 airlines take advantage of the UAE's open skies policy, operating to and from over 220 destinations. Listed below are the local airlines, many of which offer business class, as well as budget airlines operating out of the UAE's airports.

Emirates

Air Arabia *airarabia.com*
Emirates *emirates.com*
Etihad Airways 02 511 0000, *etihadairways.com*
flydubai 04 231 1000, *flydubai.com*
Gulf Air 04 271 6207, *gulfair.com*
Jazeera Airways 04 217 7506, *jazeeraairways.com*
Qatar Airways 04 231 9921, *qatarairways.com*
Wizz Air *wizzair.com*

Taxis (Abu Dhabi)
National Taxi 02 554 8868, *nationaltaxi.ae*
TransAD 600 5353 53, *transad.ae*

Taxis (Dubai)
Cars Taxi Services 04 269 3344, *carstaxi.ae*
Dubai Taxi Corporation 04 208 0808, *dtc.dubai.ae*
Ladies Taxi 04 208 0808, *dtc.dubai.ae*
National Taxi 04 339 0002, *nationaltaxi.ae*

Taxis (Northern Emirates)
Citi Taxi 06 533 3550, *stc.gov.ae*
Union Taxi 06 532 5333, *stc.gov.ae*

Car Hire
Avis 800 AVIS, *avis.ae*
Budget Rent A Car 800 2722, *budget-uae.com*
Car Fare Rent A Car 800 CAR FARE, *carfarellc.com*
Diamondlease Car Rental 800 DRIVE, *diamondlease.com*
Dollar Rent A Car 04 224 4855, *dollaruae.com*
Europcar 800 EUROPCAR, *europcardubai.com*
EuroStar Rent A Car 04 266 1117, *eurostarrental.com*
German Rent A Car 600 548 887, *germanrac.com*
Hertz 800 HERTZ, *hertzuae.com*
National Car Rental 04 440 1266, *national-ae.com*
Patriot Rent A Car 04 224 4244, *patriotdubai.com*
Sixt Rent-A-Car 04 347 9777, *sixt-uae.com*
Thrifty Car Rental 800 4770, *thriftyuae.com*

Chauffeur/Private Driver Services
Buddys Designated Drivers 800 283397, buddys.ae
Careem 04 440 5222, *careem.com*
Connection Chauffeur 04 346 9893, *limo-uae.com*
Dubai Executive Chauffeurs 800 7277, *dubaiexecutivechauffeur.com*
Safer Driver 800 72337, *saferdriver.ae*
The Driver 800 831, *thedriver.ae*
Uber *uber.com*

CURRENTLY, OVER
100 AIRLINES TAKE
ADVANTAGE OF THE
UAE'S OPEN SKIES
POLICY, OPERATING TO
AND FROM OVER 220
DESTINATIONS

HOTELS

There is a great variety of business hotels in the UAE, ranging from budget to luxury, beachfront to business district, and, with many offering business facilities and equipment, there is a choice of locations for business events, overnight conferences and ad hoc meetings. See askexplorer.com for comprehensive listings.

Abu Dhabi

The capital has no shortage of hotels to choose from, and most hotels here are geared more towards business travellers.

Aloft Abu Dhabi

02 654 5000, *aloftabudhabi.com*

Attached to Abu Dhabi National Exhibition Centre (ADNEC), trendy Aloft is more functional in style than the plusher Hyatt Capital Gate nearby, but nevertheless comfortable within its 408 rooms and suites. These include 42" LCD screens, free wi-fi and a sizeable work desk area. Even on the poolside deck, the wi-fi facilities allow business guests to relax while shooting off a few last-minute emails.

Cristal Salam Hotel

02 659 7666, *cristalhospitality.com*

This four-star, 112-room hotel is located within Abu Dhabi's banking district. It offers a business centre, executive lounge, free high-speed internet access (both wi-fi and wired), and four boardroom spaces on the 10th floor. There are plenty of leisure facilities, including an outdoor pool, plus a Korean restaurant with two karaoke rooms!

Crowne Plaza Abu Dhabi

800 4642, *ihg.com*

Located within the Hamdan Bin Mohammed Street commerce area, this hotel describes itself as the perfect place for visiting and doing business with a business centre and technology-enabled boardrooms. Wi-fi is free to IHG Rewards Club members. Restaurants include Asian and Italian, while guests can make use of the pool and fitness centre. Another location on Yas Island also has a business centre, and is surrounded by the capital's biggest attractions.

Eastern Mangroves Hotel & Spa by Anantara

02 656 1000, *anantara.com*

This 222-room, 5-star oasis of calm sits amidst Abu Dhabi's protected mangroves district. It is just 15 minutes from Abu Dhabi International Airport and 10 minutes away from downtown. It offers a business centre and five fully configured meeting rooms. There's also a gorgeous infinity pool and state-of-the art fitness centre, and the spa is said to be the best in the capital.

Hilton Abu Dhabi

02 681 1900, *hilton.com*
Conveniently located between Abu Dhabi's financial district and Marina Mall, with a private beach and three pools. There are 327 guest rooms, plenty of award-winning restaurants, bars and lounges, and 14 fully equipped meeting rooms. There is also a modern business centre in the lobby area.

Hyatt Capital Gate Abu Dhabi

02 596 1234, *abudhabi.capitalgate.hyatt.com*
Located in the quirky Capital Gate Building (the world's 'most leaning' building with an 18 degree tilt), this is a major business centre adjoining ADNEC. It is 15 minutes from Abu Dhabi International Airport and 10 minutes from the twofour54 media free zone. There's a spa and a state-of-the-art fitness centre.

Jumeirah at Etihad Towers, Abu Dhabi

02 811 5555, *jumeirah.com*
Located at the southern end of the Corniche with both a business and resort-like ambience. With some of the best views in town, rooms include serviced residences for longer stays. The business centre has meeting rooms, a well-equipped conference centre and ballroom. Leisure offerings include excellent restaurants.

THE CAPITAL HAS NO SHORTAGE OF HOTELS TO CHOOSE FROM, AND MOST ARE GEARED MORE TOWARDS BUSINESS TRAVELLERS

Jumeirah at Etihad Towers

Royal Rose Hotel By City Seasons

02 672 4000, *royalrosehotel.com*
This plush offering located in the commercial district will impress for its rather baroque, over-the-top decor. Its 350 rooms are grand with good amenities, and there's a rooftop pool for some relaxation. Meeting rooms are well-equipped.

Sofitel Abu Dhabi Corniche

02 813 7777, *sofitel.com*
Located in the middle of the city's business district, Sofitel offers a touch of class with modern elegance. Rooms are comfortable – upgrade to a suite for added extras such as a butler and club lounge access. Dining options here are top notch, and there's plenty of technology-enabled events and meetings space.

Downtown

Armed Forces Officers Club & Hotel 800 23624, *afoc.mil.ae*
City Seasons Al Hamra Hotel Abu Dhabi 02 672 5000, *cityseasonsgroup.com*
Cristal Hotel Abu Dhabi 02 652 0000, *cristalhotelsandresorts.com*
Crowne Plaza Abu Dhabi 800 4642, *ichotelsgroup.com*
Dusit Thani Abu Dhabi 02 698 8888, *dusit.com*
Grand Millennium Al Wahda 02 443 9999, *millenniumhotels.com*

Yas Viceroy Hotel, Abu Dhabi

Hilton Capital Grand Abu Dhabi 02 617 0000, *hilton.com*
One to One Hotel The Village 02 495 2000, *onetoonehotels.com*
Park Rotana Abu Dhabi 02 657 3333, *rotana.com*
The Ritz-Carlton Abu Dhabi Grand Canal 02 818 8888, *ritzcarlton.com*
Rosewood Abu Dhabi 02 813 5550, *rosewoodhotels.com*
Sands Hotel 02 615 6666, *sands.danahotels.com*

Yas Island, Saadiyat Island

Crowne Plaza Abu Dhabi Yas Island 02 656 3000, *ihg.com*
Park Hyatt Abu Dhabi Hotel & Villas 02 407 1234, *hyatt.com*
Radisson Blu Hotel Abu Dhabi Yas Island 02 656 2000, *radissonblu.com*
Yas Island Rotana 02 656 4000, *rotana.com*
Yas Viceroy Abu Dhabi 02 656 0000, *viceroyhotelsandresorts.com*

Close To Abu Dhabi International Airport

Al Raha Beach Hotel 02 508 0555, *alrahabeach.danahotels.com*
Fairmont Bab Al Bahr 02 654 3333, *fairmont.com*
Golden Tulip Al Jazira Hotel & Resort 02 562 9100, *goldentulipaljazira.com*
Holiday Inn Abu Dhabi 02 657 4888, *holidayinn.com*
Hotel Novotel Abu Dhabi Al Bustan 02 501 6444, *novotel.com*
Mafraq Hotel 02 659 6666, *mafraq-hotel.com*
Novotel Abu Dhabi Gate Hotel 02 508 9999, *novotel.com*
Shangri-La Hotel Qaryat Al Beri 02 509 8888, *shangri-la.com*
The Westin Abu Dhabi Golf Resort & Spa 02 616 9999, *westinabudhabigolfresort.com*
Traders Hotel Qaryat Al Beri 02 510 8888, *shangri-la.com*

Corniche Area

Beach Rotana 800 7744, *rotana.com*
Emirates Palace Hotel 02 690 9000, *kempinski.com*
InterContinental Abu Dhabi 02 666 6888, *intercontinental.com*
Khalidiya Palace Rayhaan By Rotana 02 657 0000, *rotana.com*
Le Meridien Abu Dhabi 02 644 6666, *lemeridienabudhabi.com*
Le Royal Meridien Abu Dhabi 02 674 2020, *leroyalmeridienabudhabi.com*
Millennium Hotel Abu Dhabi 02 614 6000, *millenniumhotels.com*
Oryx Hotel 02 681 0001, *oryxhotel.ae*
The Royal Hotel Abu Dhabi 02 815 2222, *theroyalhotelabudhabi.com*
Sheraton Abu Dhabi Hotel & Resort 02 677 3333, *sheratonabudhabihotel.com*
Sheraton Khalidiya Hotel Abu Dhabi 02 666 6220
St Regis Corniche Abu Dhabi 02 694 4444, *stregisabudhabi.com*

Dubai

The thousands of hotels in Dubai cater to all budgets and business needs.

The Address Downtown Dubai

04 436 8888, *theaddress.com*

A great location next to the world's tallest building, Burj Khalifa, and the world's largest shopping centre, Dubai Mall, the 63-storey high Address Downtown has 196 rooms from studio-size to 4-bedroom penthouse residences. Each has good connectivity, an iPod docking station, large flat-screen TV and plush marble-finished bathrooms. Meeting spaces cater for small gatherings through to large-scale events.

Hyatt Place Dubai, Deira

04 608 1234, *dubaialrigga.place.hyatt.com*

This stylish and modern hotel is good for business and close to Downtown Dubai and Trade Centre. Any business traveller will feel right at home – wi-fi is free throughout the hotel, and the light, stylish rooms have ample space for both working and sleeping, along with a cosy corner to take a break. The menu of essentials available to order, ranging from toothbrushes to phone chargers, is a nice touch.

Festival City, Dubai

ONE OF DUBAI'SMOST ESTABLISHED BUSINESS HOTELS, LE MERIDIEN DUBAI HOTEL & CONFERENCE CENTRE IS A HISTORICAL CHOICE FOR THOSE THAT NEED TO BE BASED LITERALLY A STONE'S THROW FROM THE AIRPORT

Hotel Ibis World Trade Centre

04 332 4444, *ibis.com*

Dubai International Convention & Exhibition Centre, which hosts trade exhibitions across a diverse range of industries on a year-round basis, has this functional 4-star city centre hotel onsite, and a stone's throw from the metro station. All 210 rooms have wi-fi, and there's a complimentary shuttle service to all major malls and Jumeira beach.

InterContinental, Dubai Festival City

04 701 1111, *ichotelsgroup.com*

A great location very close to the airport and retail complex Dubai Festival City, with a business centre and 13 fully-equipped meeting rooms of varying sizes. It is convenient for traditional attractions such as Dubai Creek and the famous Gold Souk, while golfers can take on the nearby championship 18 hole Al Badia course.

Jumeirah Creekside Hotel

04 230 8555, *jumeirah.com*

This is a unique concept in terms of its design as an art hotel. The 482 pieces of Middle Eastern contemporary art displayed throughout the property and 292 rooms were specially commissioned to 51 regional artists. Rooms all display their own unique artwork and are simply but distinctively designed. TVs are laptop connectable and the desk has a full, easy-to-access plug station. 25 meeting rooms are fully equipped with the latest technology.

Melia Dubai

04 386 8111, *melia-dubai.com*

The region's first Spanish 5-star hotel, located in the bustling Bur Dubai district and a short drive away from the main business towers of Sheikh Zayed Road and Business Bay. Melia offers complimentary wi-fi, a rooftop swimming pool, spa and the award-winning restaurant Signature by Sanjeev Kapoor. Board and meeting rooms offer the full range of technology and food and beverage requirements.

Le Meridien Dubai Hotel & Conference Centre

04 217 0000, *lemeridien-dubai.com*

One of Dubai's most established business hotels. It is a historical choice for those that need to be based literally a stone's throw from the airport and close to many of the city's business districts. Business travellers can make use of 12 function rooms with full technology support. There are also four outdoor temperature-controlled pools, spa, health club and flood-lit tennis courts.

Novotel World Trade Centre Hotel

04 332 0000, *novotel.com*
The 412-room Novotel is a two-minute walk from Dubai
International Convention & Exhibition Centre. It has an outdoor
swimming pool, gym, beauty salon, choice of restaurants/bars
and in-room wi-fi.

Ramada Jumeirah

04 702 7000, *ramadajumeirah.ae*
This 4-star hotel is ten minutes from Dubai World Trade Centre
and just 15 minutes from the airport. Leisure facilities include a
pool and restaurants. Its 252 modern guestrooms have wi-fi, and
meeting rooms are equipped with full audiovisual technology.
Business travellers can also make use of the business centre.

Ritz-Carlton DIFC

04 372 2222, *ritzcarlton.com*
Well-located within DIFC, the Ritz-Carlton has 341 guestrooms,
all with high-speed internet. It's just five minutes' walk from two
metro stations and around 20 minutes' drive from the airport,
and it has eight function rooms and a ballroom. Along with its
compliment of restaurants and lounges are indoor and outdoor
heated swimming pools, a spa and 24-hour fitness centre.

Sheraton Dubai Mall of the Emirates

Sheraton Dubai Mall of the Emirates Hotel

04 377 2000, *sheratondubaimalloftheemirates.com*
Conveniently close to a number of major free zones including
Dubai Internet City, Dubai Media City and TECOM, this hotel is also
connected to one of Dubai's flagship shopping malls. Its nine
meeting spaces are fully-equipped with audiovisual equipment.

Close To Dubai International Airport

Crowne Plaza Dubai Festival City 04 701 2222, *ihg.com*
Dubai International Hotel Terminal 1 & 3 04 224 4000,
dubaiintlhotels.com
Holiday Inn Express Dubai Airport 04 290 0111, *hiexpress.com*
Millennium Airport Hotel 04 702 8888, *millenniumhotels.com*
Park Hyatt Dubai 04 602 1234, *dubai.park.hyatt.com*
Premier Inn Dubai International Airport 04 260 4000, *global.*
premierinn.com
Shangri-La Hotel Dubai 04 343 8888, *shangri-la.com*
Sheraton Dubai Creek Hotel & Towers 04 228 1111,
sheratondubaicreek.com
Hilton Dubai Creek 04 227 1111, *hilton.com*

Downtown Dubai, DIFC, Trade Centre

Al Manzil Downtown Dubai 04 428 5888, *almanzilhotel.ae*
Crowne Plaza Hotel Sheikh Zayed Road 04 331 1111, *ihg.com*
Dusit Thani Dubai 04 343 3333, *dusit.com*
Fairmont Dubai 04 332 5555, *fairmont.com*
Jumeirah Emirates Towers 04 330 0000, *jumeirah.com*
JW Marriott Marquis Hotel 04 414 0000,
jwmarriottmarquisdubai.com
Radisson Blu Hotel Downtown 04 450 2000, *radissonblu.com*
Sofitel Dubai Downtown 04 338 7521, *sofitel.com*
The H Hotel Dubai 04 501 8888, *h-hotel.com*
Vida Downtown Dubai 04 420 6088, *vida hotels.com*

Beachfront

Anantara Dubai The Palm Resort & Spa 04 567 8888,
anantara.com
Dubai Marine Beach Resort & Spa 04 346 1111, *dxbmarine.com*
Habtoor Grand Beach Resort & Spa 04 399 5000,
habtoorhotels.com
Le Meridien Mina Seyahi Beach Resort & Marina 04 399 3333,
lemeridien-minaseyahi.com
Mina A'Salam 04 366 8888, *jumeirah.com*
Sofitel Dubai Palm Jumeirah Resort & Spa 04 455 6677,
sofitel.com
Waldorf Astoria Dubai Palm Jumeirah 04 818 2222 ,
waldorfastoria3.hilton.com

Sharjah

The culture capital of the UAE has plenty of affordable options.

Centro Sharjah

06 508 8000, *rotana.com*
This hotel claims to be for the 'budget-conscious business traveller'. It is positioned next to the airport and 15 minutes from Sharjah City Centre and its business districts. Its 306 rooms and suites all have high-speed wi-fi. There are two technology-enabled meeting rooms, a business centre, swimming pool, gym and dining options.

Radisson Blu Resort Sharjah

06 565 7777, *radissonblu.com*
This property is very much a combined business hotel and resort, with 306 rooms, a private beach and free high-speed internet. It is located just 15km from Sharjah International Airport and 18km from Dubai International Airport. Meeting and conference facilities include internet connectivity, LCD and overhead projectors, audiovisual equipment and a meetings/events team to assist you through the process. Seven meeting rooms/boardrooms accommodate 14-80 people.

Ramada Sharjah

06 530 0003, *ramadasharjah.com*
Located 15-30 minutes from both Sharjah and Dubai International Airports with an airport shuttle service. It was given the Best 4-Star Business/Corporate Hotel – Silver Award at the MENA Travel Awards 2014. Offering one and two bedroom apartments, it has a fitness centre and swimming pool. As well as a 24-hour business centre, it has 55 sq m of boardroom-style meeting space, equipped with audiovisual equipment, food and beverage services and event planning where required.

72 By Hues 06 507 9797, *hueshotels.com*
Al Bustan Hotel 06 528 5444, *albustangroup.com*
Al Hamra Hotel 06 516 0000, *alhamrahotel.net*
Al Hayat Hotel Suites 06 593 2999, *alhayatsuites.com*
Copthorne Hotel 06 593 0555, *millenniumhotels.ae*
Coral Beach Resort 800 267 25, *coral-beachresortsharjah.com*
Ewan Hotel Sharjah 06 528 0111, *ewanhotel.ae*
Golden Tulip Sharjah 06 519 7777, *goldentulipsharjah.com*
Grand Excelsior Sharjah 800 464 2, *grandexcelsioralsharjah.com*
Hilton Sharjah 06 519 2222, *hilton.com*
Sharjah Carlton Hotel 06 528 3711, *mhgroupsharjah.com*
Sharjah Grand Hotel 06 528 5557, *sharjahgrand.com*
Sharjah Rotana 06 563 7777, *rotana.com*

Northern Emirates

Enjoy some of the country's best scenery and beaches.

Hilton Ras Al Khaimah Resort and Spa

07 228 8844 *hilton.com*

A beachfront property around an hour's drive from Dubai International Airport. Its 475 rooms all have internet access. There is audiovisually-equipped meeting space for up to 80-150 guests. Other facilities include four 'speciality' restaurants, a 24-hour fitness centre, outdoor swimming pools, a tennis court and water sports centre. It was voted best Relaxation & Spa in the Middle East TripAdvisor Travellers' Choice Awards 2013.

Waldorf Astoria Ras Al Khaimah

07 203 5555, *waldorfastoria3. hilton.com*

Winner of a number of awards including a Business Traveller Middle East award in 2014, the gorgeous Waldorf Astoria Ras Al Khaimah is set on a private beach, has two outdoor pools and a nearby 18 hole championship golf course. Meeting spaces are equipped with all technological mod cons and cater for smaller groups through to high-end corporate events. It also claims to be the perfect location for team-building events. Its restaurants are superb.

Waldorf Astoria Ras Al Khaimah

Ramada Beach Hotel Ajman

06 742 9999, *ramada.com*
Located on the Corniche, guest rooms at the Ramada Beach Hotel Ajman are fully-fitted suites with one or more bedrooms, all with kitchenette and dining area. All suites have international direct dialling, satellite TV and balconies with sea views. Meeting spaces range from boardroom to seminar-size. All are soundproofed and technology-enabled. Dining includes the King Grill and Flavours restaurants. There is a complimentary shuttle bus to local attractions, while the Shapes Spa and Health Club offers the chance for some prime relaxation.

Ajman Saray

06 714 2222, *ajmansaray.com*
Also within Ajman's business centre, Ajman Saray's 205 guest rooms offer a work desk, international direct dialling, voicemail and 40" LED TV, while their floor-to-ceiling windows let in plenty of natural light. Its meeting spaces provide views of the Arabian Gulf and comprise seven rooms equipped with audiovisual equipment. Restaurants and lounges include seafood, Mediterranean and Lebanese flavours, plus a beach bar and grill.

Radisson Blu Resort Fujairah

09 244 9700, *radissonblu.com*
Its pastel exterior might be an acquired taste, but the modern, corporate interior and wonderful restaurants that lie within, make this hotel a bit of a treat for the senses. The whole place is reminiscent of a spa, with clean lines and wholesome colours - in fact, there actually is a wonderful Japanese spa, as well as a spacious private beach.

Fujairah Rotana Resort & Spa

09 244 9888, *rotana.com*
This beachfront hotel on Fujairah's Al Aqah coastline has 250 rooms of different sizes, all equipped with a high-speed internet connection, international direct dialling, satellite TV, and other amenities. Its three smaller meeting rooms through to larger conferencing facilities cater for small private gatherings through to seminars. There is a dedicated events team to hand if required. The hotel has six restaurants and lounges, a spa and lots of other leisure facilities.

Ajman

The Ajman Palace 800 26725, *theajmanpalace.com*
Belfort Hotel 06 741 8001,
Crown Palace Hotel 06 740 9111, *crownpalace.me*
Dream Palace Hotel 06 741 7070, *dreampalacehotel.net*

Emirates Plaza 06 744 5777
Fairmont Ajman *fairmont.com*
Kempinski Hotel Ajman 06 714 5555, *kempinski.com*
Tulip Inn Royal Suites Ajman 06 741 3777, *tulipinnajman.com*

Fujairah
Al Diar Siji Hotel 09 223 2000, *aldiarhotels.com*
City Plaza Hotel 09 222 2202, *phoenixhotelsgroup.com*
City Tower Hotel 09 223 6888, *fortune-hotels.net*
Concorde By Mourouj Fujairah 09 224 9000, *concordefujairah.com*
Fairmont Fujairah *fairmont.com*
Hilton Fujairah Resort 09 222 2411, *hilton.com*
Le Meridien Al Aqah Beach Resort 09 244 9000, *lemeridien-alaqah.com*
Novotel Fujairah 09 223 9999, *novotel.com*

Ras Al Khaimah
The Cove Rotana Resort 800 774 4, *rotana.com*
Banyan Tree Ras Al Khaimah Beach 07 206 7777, *banyantree.com*
DoubleTree by Hilton Ras Al Khaimah 07 226 0666, *doubletree3.hilton.com*

Radisson Blu Resort, Fujairah

BUSINESS DO'S & DON'TS

Like anywhere in the world, doing business in the UAE has its own unique idiosyncrasies. Even if you work for a Western company, the chances are that some of your business transactions will be with Emiratis, whether on a customer or client basis.

Dress Sensibly

It's a good idea to dress conservatively for business meetings. Men are advised to wear a smart suit and tie, and women should at the very least cover knees and shoulders. Certain government departments, especially in the capital, have an extremely conservative dress code, so it would be advisable for women to be extra sensitive with their dress.

Handshake – Or Not?

When meeting someone of the opposite sex it's likely that a handshake will not be given and is best to refrain unless they extend their hand to you. Always use your right hand to meet, eat or hand over items as Muslims reserve the left hand for bodily hygiene and consider it unclean.

Nose Kiss

A nose kiss is a customary greeting in the UAE but is only used between close friends and associates, and you should not attempt to greet someone in this way.

Arabic coffeepot

Kahwa

If you're attending a business meeting at an Arab-owned company, it's likely that you'll be served traditional Arabic coffee, or kahwa. Sharing coffee is an important social ritual in the Middle East so you should drink some when offered. Cups should be taken in the right hand and if there is a waiter standing by, replenishing your cup, there are two ways to signal that you have had enough: either leave a small amount of coffee in the bottom of your cup or gently tip the cup from side to side.

Patience

Things may move more slowly and decisions take longer than you may be used to. Keeping in regular contact with your clients helps to maintain genial relations, and picking up the phone rather than relying on email can make the world of difference.

Small Talk

Avoid enquiring about family matters and concentrate on more generic conversations such as general compliments about the country if you are newly arrived. It's polite to send greetings to a person's family but avoid enquiring after female family members though, as this is kept extremely private. Avoid showing the bottom of your shoes in meetings too as this is considered an insult.

Ramadan

The Holy Month marks a general slowdown in the business world, when all workers are entitled to shortened working hours. Be prepared to factor in extra time for any business dealings during this period. At the end of Ramadan, business comes to a halt for the Eid al Fitr holiday.

Gifts

It's not a requirement to bring gifts to associates in the UAE, but a small gesture would only be received well. A memento from your home country is an ice breaker in any business situation.

Lingo

A simple 'Aleykum-u-Asalaam' is a nice gesture when meeting Emirati associates, even if that's where your knowledge of Arabic ends.

It's Friday

Friday is the holiest day in Islam, and is not a working day in the UAE. Don't expect to hear from your UAE associates on this day.

SHARING COFFEE IS AN IMPORTANT SOCIAL RITUAL IN THE MIDDLE EAST SO YOU SHOULD REALLY DRINK SOME WHEN OFFERED

MICE

THE UAE'S CENTRAL LOCATION MEANS WORLDWIDE ORGANISATIONS ARE INCREASINGLY CHOOSING THE COUNTRY AS A DYNAMIC AND WELL-PLACED MEETING POINT

MORE THAN
100
AIRLINES FLY
INTO DUBAI

ADNEC AND
DWTC HOST
HUNDREDS OF
HUGE INDUSTRY
EVENTS

The Meetings, Incentives, Conferencing & Exhibitions (MICE) industry in the UAE is growing rapidly, as both local and international companies choose to host events in the country. Offering superb transport links and a wide choice of stunning venues, both Dubai and Abu Dhabi are popular locations for international trade fairs and conferences. Ras Al Khaimah (RAK) is also coming of age with new hotels and business facilities opening as the northern emirate pushes ahead with its $20 billion tourism regeneration plan.

As emerging markets continue to drive the global economy, the UAE's proximity to the Middle East, Africa, India and the Far East means worldwide organisations are increasingly choosing the country as a dynamic and well-placed meeting point.

RAS AL KHAIMAH (RAK) IS ALSO COMING OF AGE WITH NEW HOTELS AND BUSINESS FACILITIES OPENING AS THE NORTHERN EMIRATE PUSHES AHEAD WITH A $20 BILLION TOURISM REGENERATION PLAN

Abu Dhabi

There are a growing number of industry and trade events in Abu Dhabi that are lucrative for companies – or a fantastic day of entertainment for local families. According to the Abu Dhabi Tourism and Culture Authority, the direct economic impact of MICE business events on the emirate is expected to grow at seven per cent annually to Dhs.5.1 billion by 2020.

In addition to ADNEC, and an abundance of well-equipped business hotels in the emirate, Abu Dhabi offers unique MICE facilities at Ferrari World (host to the world's largest incentives group in 2014, a delegation of 14,500 people from China) and Yas Marina Circuit, home of the Abu Dhabi Grand Prix.

Dubai

The bustling and cosmopolitan city of Dubai has proved a huge draw for business folk from around the world. More than 100 different airlines fly into the city, readily connecting Dubai to vast swathes of the globe. All the major hotel chains are well represented in the emirate offering a large inventory to accommodate and cater events of any size, often complemented by state-of-the-art production facilities. From the sprawling ballrooms of Atlantis, The Palm, to the Armani Hotel terrace with views of the Burj Khalifa, to luxurious beach palaces, and budget options in the smaller hotels, the choice is unrivalled in the Middle East.

Northern Emirates

The northern emirates' growing portfolio of hotels offers sleek business facilities in quiet and rugged desert surroundings. Standout offerings include the Waldorf Astoria Ras Al Khaimah, while venues in Fujairah and Sharjah have plentiful facilities.

EVENTS & EXHIBITIONS

Throughout the UAE there are exhibitions and trade shows serving pretty much any industry you could think of, from tanks to toys, cotton to confectionery. We've rounded up some of the biggest events that take place, organised by emirate.

Abu Dhabi

The majority of Abu Dhabi's events take place at the capital's largest venue, Abu Dhabi National Exhibition Centre (ADNEC), which hosts everything from fashion shows to energy summits. Each year ADNEC hosts more than 100 events, bringing millions of dollars to the city.

Asian Business Research Conference
asmmr.com

This conference will cover areas like accounting & finance, advertising management, management information system, project management organisational behaviour, entrepreneurship & technical innovation, business research in gulf region, and human resource management.

Cityscape Abu Dhabi
cityscapeabudhabi.com

Cityscape Abu Dhabi, the international property investment & development event – is an annual networking exhibition and

Arabian Travel Market

conference focusing on all aspects of the property development cycle. Look forward to big announcements on the latest city planning developments.

Gulf Incentive Business Travel & Meetings
gibtm.com

GIBTM is the Middle East's only dedicated business platform, connecting the region's inbound and outbound MICE and Business Travel industry through face-to-face meetings, pre-scheduled appointments, knowledge and networking.

SIAL The Middle Eastern Food Exhibition
02 401 2949, sialme.com

Held in strategic partnership with Abu Dhabi Food Control Authority, this is the region's fastest growing professional business platform for the food, drink and hospitality industries.

Tawdheef Exhibition
02 493 5103, tawdheef.ae

Leading recruitment exhibition that focuses on Employment and Career Development for UAE Nationals. Tawdheef is the ideal exhibition for companies that are keen to develop their UAE national workforce by meeting talented jobseekers and professionals and boosting their Emiratisation drive.

Dubai

In the past few years, Dubai has really proved its mettle as an events location. As well as hosting stalwart events such as tech mega fair GITEX and the world's largest travel trade event, Arabian Travel Market, the emirate is increasingly drawing high-profile names and hosting respected global trade conferences. In another nod to Dubai's growing events clout, the emirate has also become a popular launch pad for worldwide product launches, such as smartphones.

The Dubai World Trade Centre (DWTC) is the emirate's largest venue, hosting more than 500 events every year, and receiving more than 1.4 million visitors and 6,000 exhibitors annually.

Arab Future Cities Summit
smartcitiesdubai.com

The Middle East's premier smart cities event takes place at the luxurious Sofitel Dubai The Palm Resort & Spa. The region's senior city stakeholders, high-profile government authorities and cutting-edge technologists representing the world's leading smart city brands will gather to address key projects and initiatives in smart urban development.

Arabian Travel Market
arabiantravelmarket.com
Arabian Travel Market is the travel and tourism event unlocking business potential within the Middle East for inbound and outbound tourism professionals.

Automechanika Dubai
automechanikame.com
A trading link to markets difficult to reach, this trade fair is a good platform to find out more about new products, find new suppliers and compare product alternatives.

Careers UAE
04 308 6941, careersuae.ae
This event has played a key role in achieving the vision of the country's leadership, particularly in the area of Emiratisation.

Cityscape Global
cityscapeglobal.com
Cityscape is the annual opportunity to build and maintain your presence across Middle East real estate markets.

Dubai International Brand Licensing Fair
licensingdubai.ae
The Middle East's only brand licensing marketplace featuring a vast collection of properties and brands. It is the perfect meeting place to build partnerships, get preview of the newest licensing and merchandising programs and sign licensing deals.

GITEX Technology Week
gitex.com
GITEX is the ICT business gateway to the Middle East, North Africa and South Asia Region. GITEX's role in the ICT industry is pivotal for the re-export market. It is an annual international trading hub for the global technology sector. GITEX acts as both an inbound sourcing platform for the Middle East and the eminent source for anyone doing business in the region.

Gulfood
gulfood.com
Gulfood provides a trade and sourcing platform without equal, where international flavours find world-class business.

Innovation Arabia
innovationarabia.ae
Innovation Arabia helps to capitalise on the successes and the potential of this community; it will help to unleash the

economic opportunities waiting within the region. Innovation Arabia features four important tracks, namely; Quality and Business Management, E-Learning Excellence, Health & Environment, and Islamic Banking & Finance.

Middle East Exclusive
middleeastexclusive.com
MEE-Dubai is the high-growth retail event supported by the world's most successful duty free retailer Dubai Duty Free. This unique trade fair brings together product suppliers from around the world and leading retail buyers.

Smart Living City
smartlivingcity.com
Smart Living City Dubai is an event to accelerate smart business programs in Dubai. This event brings the best of technology and the best practitioners across continents to the fore. It provides them with the unique opportunity to share their ideas with government representatives, company executives, technology investors and business accelerators.

Sharjah
Sharjah Expo Centre hosts several lucrative events throughout the year.

MidEast Watch & Jewellery Show
mideastjewellery.com
A bi-annual regional platform that offers jewellers the best possible reach and response from a highly receptive target audience.

Chinese Commodities Fair Sharjah
ccfs.ae
A chance to check out the latest products and developments from thousands of Chinese companies.

Halal Middle East
halalfoodme.com
A unique exhibition that caters to food and food products that are manufactured and distributed according to halal requirements.

Green Middle East
green-middleeast.com
The regional exhibition for the environment industry in the Middle East. It will see participation from top business houses from the energy sector.

VENUES & FACILITIES

There's a huge array of venues in the UAE for hosting coporate events of any size. Most hotels have meetings and conference facilities, and you can find information on these in the Business Travel section earlier in this chapter. Listed here are alternative venues, from the country's biggest exhibition centres to the more unique facilities.

Abu Dhabi

ADNEC is the capital's largest exhibition space with all kinds of facilities, but there are also some great options for adding some excitement to a corporate event.

Abu Dhabi Golf Club
02 558 8990, adgolfclub.com
Has three state-of-the-art meeting and conference rooms of contemporary design allowing the club to cater for a variety of events, from smaller meetings to corporate banquets. There is also a large outdoor terrace for cocktail receptions.

Abu Dhabi National Exhibition Centre (ADNEC)
800 23632, adnec.ae
This sophisticated, avante-garde convention centre is rapidly becoming a premier trade show location in the Middle East and welcomes over one million visitors each year. Along with the vast exhibition halls, there are facilities for smaller events, meetings and conferences.

Ferrari World
02 496 8001, ferrariworldabudhabi.com
Ferrari World is an exciting and unique venue offering over 3,000m² of meeting space. There are function rooms able to accommodate groups from 15 to 250 guests. It's also possible to hire the facilities and attractions for large-scale events.

Manarat Al Saadiyat
02 657 5800, saadiyat.ae
Literally meaning 'the place of enlightenment', this is a 15,400m² visitor centre designed to bring the vision of the island to life through the Saadiyat story. The venue includes four gallery spaces, an auditorium, four meeting rooms, a large atrium and a great restaurant and coffee bar.

Yas Marina Circuit
02 659 9393, yasmarinacircuit.com
The home of the Abu Dhabi F1 Grand Prix can accommodate any size event from large-scale banquets, conferences and exhibitions to small private parties. Multi-purpose indoor venue space offers spectacular views of the track and marina. Outdoor venue space for hire includes part or the entire F1 track. The driving experience packages provide a unique corporate day out.

Dubai

Dubai International Convention and Exhibition Centre (DICEC) is a leading venue for global events.

Bateaux Dubai

04 399 4994, jaresortshotels.com
This traditional dhow cruises along the spectacular Dubai Creek and offers tailor-made cruises for corporate events such as product launches, press conferences and cocktail parties. It can accommodate up to 300 guests.

Dubai World Trade Centre

04 332 1000, dwtc.com
Host to some of the world's most high profile events, Dubai World Trade Centre offers more than 92,000m^2 of multi-purpose space with DICEC at the heart of the complex. The halls offer flexible, open spaces, while for smaller, more intimate events there is a wide range of meeting rooms.

The Fridge

04 347 7793, thefridgedubai.com
Located in a warehouse in the heart of Dubai's art hub, The Fridge is a contemporary and dynamic event venue that can hold up to 250 people. The Fridge provides an urban, edgy alternative to the more traditional offerings.

Majlis Gallery

04 353 6233, themajlisgallery.com
The Majlis Gallery is a fine art gallery situated in the old Bastakiya district of Dubai. The beautiful Majlis Gallery Courtyard is available for corporate private functions to companies who provide sponsorship to the Gallery.

Northern Emirates

Look north for something even more unique.

Bedouin Oasis Camp (Ras Al Khaimah)

04 266 6020, arabianincentive.com
This desert camp offers a traditional experience fused with luxury, and with a special focus on tailor-made activities. It can be hired on an exclusive basis for events under the stars.

Sharjah Expo Centre

06 577 0000, expo-centre.ae
With state-of-the-art facilities, Expo Centre offers 128,000 m^2 of floor space and is an ideal venue for exhibitions. There are three meeting rooms capable of seating up to 70 people.

WORKING
LIFE

THERE'S A MULTITUDE OF PLATFORMS IN THE UAE FROM WHICH YOU CAN FIND SUPPORT AND ADVICE

SMEs ACCOUNT FOR MORE THAN

40%

OF DUBAI'S WORKFORCE

LINKEDIN IS AMONGST THE TOP 10 MOST VISITED WEBSITES IN THE UAE

So you've navigated the red tape, you're the proud owner of a trade licence, and now you're raring to get out there and get on with turning your business into a commercially viable venture.

First of all, you're likely to need a little help, and there's a multitude of platforms in the UAE from which you can find support and advice, and not least opportunities for collaboration in terms of the services of your business.

Every emirate has dedicated business groups, councils and networks that organise events for entrepreneurs to meet and mingle, as well as workshops, seminars, lectures and so on, to give you the tools to grow your business within the context of the UAE and its market.

You're also likely to need to schmooze some potential clients, and we've got some ideas for great business lunch venues in Dubai and Abu Dhabi, from the casual to the downright swanky.

If you need to hire out some space to host a meeting, or even offices to use as a temporary base while you look for something more permanent, there are plenty of business centres in the UAE that offer a host of services and equipment to suit your needs.

And, if you need somewhere more creative to work, we've put together some inspiring venues where you'll have no trouble getting your head down to work with some fast wi-fi, a quality coffee, and perhaps even the company of your fellow entrepreneurs.

The UAE really is a vibrant, dynamic place in which to start up a company and there are some incredibly inspiring business people pushing the boundaries of achievement, not least within the pages of this book.

We hope you feel inspired, empowered, and ready to throw yourself into turning your unique idea into a profitable, sustainable business. It's not an easy road, but follow the steps in this book and things should become a bit more straightforward.

Ultimately, you're not alone. Whatever struggles you're facing, thousands of entrepreneurs have faced the same, so don't be afraid to ask for help, to seek out a supportive network. You might even have some words of wisdom or expertise to offer to somebody who didn't even know they needed it.

EVERY EMIRATE HAS DEDICATED BUSINESS GROUPS, COUNCILS AND NETWORKS THAT ORGANISE EVENTS FOR ENTREPRENEURS TO MEET AND MINGLE, AS WELL AS WORKSHOPS, SEMINARS, LECTURES AND SO ON, TO GIVE YOU THE TOOLS TO GROW YOUR BUSINESS

NETWORKING

Networking is more important than ever. But what are some of the best ways to network for success in the GCC – and how can specific events help increase your contacts?

It's who you know, not what you know, as the saying goes. And, in business, it's a philosophy that's become so important that your ability to network can make the crucial difference between complete success and utter failure. Networking of all kinds has taken on a new relevance and importance in recent years – and with the growth of online business networks like LinkedIn, and even social networks like Facebook and Twitter, the means of reaching out and connecting with others has taken on a whole new dimension.

In the GCC, business networking has taken off in a relatively small space of time. With its position as the gateway to three continents – each with burgeoning economies and trade – plus a growing interest in steering the local economy away from oil dependence in the UAE, there's huge potential for business growth in the region. And, because the business community in GCC countries is small and well connected, spending some time rubbing shoulders with your peers can really pay off.

DO'S & DON'TS

EVENTS

Networking events are a chance for you to learn from successful business owners – people who are several steps ahead of you in the game. Be sure to go in with an open mind and take on board the advice you are offered.

NETWORKING

- DO use every available opportunity to network. Take an interest in people at parties, events and gatherings and ask what they do, in case you could help each other in some way.
- DON'T blur the lines between business and friendship. It can lead to complications down the line.
- DO be yourself. People at networking events respond more favourably to people who come across as genuine and authentic. Avoid putting on a show or pushing a 'hard sell'.
- DON'T recommend someone if you're not sure they'd do a good job, as you risk doing damage to your own reputation.
- DO follow up on networking events. Call your contacts and see if you can take that initial conversation to the next level.
- DON'T under-dress for events. The best-dressed person often has a subliminal advantage when negotiations are taking place. Remember, first impressions last.
- DO listen! Focus on how you can help the person you're listening to rather than how they can help you. That way, the relationship is more likely to be mutually beneficial.

Given the myriad networking groups and organisations out there whose purpose it is to attract members to events, online forums, business breakfasts and seminars, effective networking takes time – so be ready to put in the legwork if you want to see results. These events are not only effective for companies seeking new alliances but entrepreneurs trying to break into an industry. Make a lasting first impression and someone you met three months ago could suddenly come knocking with an interesting opportunity for collaboration.

Remember that it's often the events with more of a 'sociable' and less of a purely 'business' angle that create the most opportunities. In fact, the most successful business networking takes place in a casual, relaxed environment, where there's less 'pitching' and more chatting. The best business networking groups actively encourage this more laid-back approach. When attending events, take a genuine interest in the other person, establish a rapport, and they're much more likely to respond and remember you than if you'd merely subjected them to a standard sales patter. Ask them topical questions about their business or industry; find out about their needs first and figure out what, if anything, you have in common.

Business Awards

Many of the business networks organise awards for start-ups and SMEs, to recognise innovation and achievement in the business world. Entering these awards is a great way to gain recognition for your brand, and to attract financial investment. Check out the Gulf Capital SME Awards organised by MEED (meedsmeawards.com), and Dubai SME 100 (dubaisme100rankings.com).

Business Groups & Councils

See also Women In Business chapter

American Business Council, Dubai & Northern Emirates
04 379 1414, *abcdubai.com*
The American Business Group 02 632 9134
Arab Business Club 04 358 3000, *arabbusinessclub.org*
Australian Business Council Dubai 04 390 0467, *abcduae.com*
Australian Business Group Abu Dhabi 050 2641 134, *ausbg.net*
British Business Group Abu Dhabi 02 445 7234,
britishbusiness.org
British Business Group Dubai & Northern Emirates
04 397 0303, *britbiz-uae.com*
Canadian Business Council Dubai 04 359 2625, *cbc-dubai.com*
Canadian Business Council Abu Dhabi 02 446 7223,
cbcabudhabi.com
Danish Business Council 050 7958 589, *danishbusinessdubai.com*

IT'S WHO YOU KNOW, NOT WHAT YOU KNOW, AS THE SAYING GOES...

Dubai Shopping Malls Group 04 358 9789, *dsmg.ae*
French Business Council Dubai & The Northern Emirates
04 312 6700, *fbcdubai.com*
French Business Group 02 674 1137, *fbgabudhabi.com*
**German Emirati Joint Council For Industry & Commerce
(AHK)** 02 645 5200, *ahk.de*
Indian Business & Professional Council 04 332 4300,
ibpcdubai.com
Iranian Business Council 04 335 9220, *ibc.ae*
Italian Business Council 04 321 3082, *italianbusinesscouncil.com*
Malaysia Business Council 04 335 5538, *mbc-uae.com*
Netherlands Business Council 050 5592 272, *nbcdubai.com*
Pakistan Business Council Dubai 04 335 9991, *pbcdubai.com*
Singapore Business Council 04 338 7336, *sbcuae.com*
South African Business Council 050 2594 280, *sabco-uae.org*
Spanish Business Council 04 427 0379,
spanishbusinesscouncil.ae
Swedish Business Council 04 429 8600, *sbcuae.se*
Swiss Business Council 04 368 7702, *swissbcuae.com*
Swiss Business Council Abu Dhabi 02 653 8181, *swissbcuae.com*
Women in Network – French Business Council 04 312 6700,
fbcdubai.com
The World Trade Club Dubai 04 309 7979, *dwtc.com*

Networking

BUSINESS CENTRES & HOT DESKS

Many business centres based in mainland UAE offer fully-furnished and serviced offices, workstations and hot desks, meeting rooms, as well as IT, administrative, postal and secretarial support – both in terms of personnel and equipment, and even breakout rooms. Free zones across the UAE also have their own business centres offering work space and services.

Business centres are widely used by start-ups and SMEs in the UAE as they offer minimal office space and set-up situations.

Abu Dhabi

The capital's business centres are strategically located in the financial hubs of the city.

Executive Business Centre
800 322 322, executivebc.net
Offices: 70
Meeting rooms: 3
On-site administrative and technology support, secretarial services including typing and presentation preparation.

Gulf Business Centre
02 678 9808, gulfbusinesscentre.info
Offices: 45
Meeting rooms: 3
Secretarial services, reception services, telephone features, fax and copier, internet, valet parking, free tea and coffee service.

International Business Center
02 681 5555, ibcuae.com
Offices: 70
Meeting rooms: 1
Standard interior, book by hour, half day or full day, availability of projector and flip chart, secretarial support.

Regus
800 734 87, regus.ae
Offices: varies
Meeting rooms: varies
Several locations in Abu Dhabi, Dubai and Sharjah. Online reservation, AV communication studios and video conferencing.

Servcorp
02 659 4100,
Meeting rooms: 2
Furnished offices, reception area, receptionist, support team, AV equipment, online booking and flexible leases.

Dubai

The city has plenty of short term office spaces and hot desks.

Alliance Business Centers
04 501 5666, abcn.ae
Offices: 58 (Deira); 168 (Silicon Oasis)
Workstations: 200 (Deira); 300 (Silicon Oasis)
Meeting rooms and conferencing facilities at two locations – The Business Village in Deira and Dubai Silicon Oasis. Onsite copy centre, executive lounge, in-house food and beverage services.

Corporate Business Services
04 383 1555, cbs-uae.ae
Offices: 10
Meeting rooms: 3
Hot and cold drinks, flip chart, whiteboards and notepads, equipment rentals for interactive and digital presentations.

MAKE Business Hub
04 392 9216, makebusinesshub.com
Workstations: 7 (each seating 4)
Meeting rooms: 3 (each seating 8)
Operates on a walk-in basis with food packages and presentation equipment.

My Office
04 455 8555, myoffice.ae
Offices: 40
Meeting rooms: 5
Workstations: 6
Full time in-house IT support, network options, electronic access cards, valet parking, mail management and phone answering.

Sentinel Business Centres
04 305 0600, sentinelbusinesscentres.com
Offices: 50
Meeting rooms: 4
Trained, professional receptionists, 24 hours to prepare your offices, conference and training rooms, video conferencing, ready to move in immediately and access to parking facilities.

Serene Business Centres
04 450 2450, serenebusinesscenters.com
Office: 50
Meeting rooms: 4
Cisco IP phone with free IVR, front desk staff, quick meeting rooms, incoming and outgoing mail management.

WORKSPACES

If you're looking for somewhere to settle down with your laptop, these work-friendly venues will keep you connected and inspired.

Most branches of the international coffee chains, such as Starbucks and Costa Coffee, offer free wi-fi and are popular places to pitch up. Here are some more interesting venues in Dubai and Abu Dhabi.

Abu Dhabi

Several of Abu Dhabi's hotels are actually popular meeting places for associates and have pleasant cafes and lobby lounges offering a suitable environment for a spot of casual work.

Cafe Arabia
02 643 9699
Spread over three floors, as well as the rooftop terrace, this tastefully decorated and unusual cafe offers light fare based on recipes the owner has collected from family and friends, as well as some inventive hot and cold beverages. Thanks to art shows and coffee mornings, this new spot has quickly established a well-deserved following among local expats. The homely feel means you'll be comfortable staying all day.

Shakespeare & Co
02 639 9626, shakespeareandco.ae
With chic Victorian flair, an eclectic menu featuring cuisines from the US, Italy and the Middle East, and period-inspired decor, this ubiquitous chain has branches around the country and offers more than just exquisite food and a relaxed atmosphere. There's wi-fi, and you won't feel unwelcome spending time with your laptop.

Dubai

With such a thriving community of freelancers, entrepreneurs and mobile business people, there are some fantastic business hubs in Dubai that nurture an innovative spirit.

The Archive
04 349 4033, thearchive.ae
Located in Safa Park, The Archive is a specialised library-cum-workspace-cum-cafe that aims at promoting a diverse and active cultural community, nurture a new generation into art, literature and education while at the same time, create a space of exploration and entertainment. Freelancers can browse books, work independently in its creative spaces and enjoy free wi-fi.

The Cribb
04 319 7645, thecribb.co

This entrepreneurial community in Al Quoz 1 is the perfect place to engage with your fellow business creatives. Workspaces are available to rent by the month, and there's an organic cafe onsite. The Cribb is the base of i360accelerator, a seed funding programme that offers a 120-day start-up acceleration to get innovative ideas off the ground. Events are also organised here.

Impact Hub Dubai
04 375 4444, dubai.new.impacthub.net

This 'innovation hub' in Downtown Dubai is part of a global platform connecting over 8,000 entrepreneurs worldwide. The facility has monthly packages for the use of workspaces and access to workshops, courses, mentors and potential investors. Free tea, coffee and snacks are offered to 'hubsters'.

MAKE Business Hub
04 392 9216, makebusinesshub.com

Located in Dubai Marina, this is an urban cafe for the mobile worker that offers a cool space where you can concentrate, and serves tasty nosh to keep the brain cells firing. MAKE is also the home of young business and provides an environment which nurtures entrepreneurship, promotes connections between like minded creatives in the UAE, and hosts events to encourage the same.

The Media Lounge
800 86563, tmlme.com

A social hub for media types, this cafe is handy for workers in Media City and has inspiring decor, wi-fi, a decent menu and also offers shisha.

The Pavilion Downtown Dubai
04 447 7025, pavilionr.ae

A non-profit contemporary art space that not only showcases new regional artists but provides a space for artists and aficionados to meet, with its restaurant, cinema, library, espresso cafe and lounge.

Shelter
04 380 9040

This free workspace is located at Warehouse 30 at Alserkal Avenue, Al Quoz 1. The aim is to nurture entrepreneurship and be an accessible community. Visit the website to sign up and join the network.

BUSINESS LUNCHES

Whether you're out to impress clients or looking for somewhere casual to conduct a working lunch, here are some of our favourite picks in Dubai and Abu Dhabi.

As much as anything, the UAE is a melting pot of different cultural flavours in terms of the range of restaurants and cafes it offers – from the most exclusive and expensive to the most casual, nutritious and delicious.

Abu Dhabi

The capital is teeming with eateries that would impress the most discerning of lunch guests, and many of the hotels offer time-conscious business lunches.

Emporio Armani Caffe

02 676 6995, altayer.com

You've got the t-shirt, worn the fragrance and now you can eat the food. Ideally situated to capture the masters of finance in Abu Dhabi's new Central Business District, the Emporio Armani Caffe clinches the deal with its gourmet Italian food and legendary pizzas. Modern and sophisticated with great views over the water, it's one cafe whose stock is rising.

The Library

02 407 1138, abudhabi.park.hyatt.com

Need a spot for an intimate meeting away from the bustling metropolis? The hushed atmosphere of the Park Hyatt's stylish tea lounge, decked with orange leather and hints of black marble, is the perfect place to mumble over the finer points of a deal while gorging on selections of home-made chocolates and pastries. Follow lunch with a head-clearing walk on the beach.

Lounge

02 596 1430, abudhabi.capitalgate.hyatt.com

Set on the 18th floor of the Hyatt Capital Gate, it's the working lunch destination of choice for those visiting ADNEC. But the elegant yet relaxed lounge-style cafe attracts people from all over; the views, pastries, snacks and premium teas are enough to convince discerning lunchers that it's worth the trip regardless. A more intimate library area is a useful place to take tea while talking over a business proposal or deal.

Market Kitchen

02 695 0300, marketkitchenabudhabi.com

The Express Lunch at this Le Royal Meridien eatery is designed to see diners in and out within one hour, so great for a speedy meeting. There's free wi-fi if you need to do a bit of work, too.

Hyatt Capital Gate Abu Dhabi

Mirabel
02 631 5111, mirabel.ae

Located in the Marks & Spencer building, Mirabel stands out from the standard shopping mall cafes; the menu encompasses delicious breakfast, lunch and dinner options made with fresh ingredients by the European-led kitchen crew.

Observation Deck At 300
02 811 5666, jumeirah.com

This smart cafe on the 74th floor of Jumeirah At Etihad Towers serves great mocktails and a high tea deserving of the name. Enjoy panoramic views of the city and have a go on the cute observation telescopes. Entrance costs Dhs.75 with Dhs.50 redeemable on food and drinks.

The Social Hub
02 447 1010

A creative environment that's ideal for the media types of the twofour54 building, the funky decor still doesn't manage to outshine the menu. Very much the spot for a casual chat, the Social Hub deals out burgers, pizzas, salads and light sandwiches. It even does special breakfast and lunch buffets for very reasonable prices.

Dubai

A host of culinary offerings in Dubai serve all types of business people, from the creative to the corporate.

1762

800 1762,1762.ae

A pleasant atmosphere to relax and enjoy artisan sandwiches, soups, salads and cakes. Its imaginative, deli-style menu features bursts of international flavours and there are homemade pies, pastries and desserts of a gourmet standard.

At.mosphere

04 888 3444, atmosphereburjkhalifa.com

With arguably the best views in town, this sky-high restaurant on the 123rd floor of the Burj Khalifa has prices to match, but the business lunch is one of the better value offerings here. It's definitely a venue to create an impression.

Elements

04 324 4252, elements-cafe.com

Vibrant yet stylish furniture and walls crammed with paintings give Elements the feel of an industrial art warehouse. Lunchtime is always a busy affair thanks to the bargain three-course buffet, while the shisha terrace fills up in the evenings as diners dig into sushi, tapas, pasta and Arabic dishes.

Jones The Grocer

04 346 6886, jonesthegrocer.com

This is more than a grocer – it's a Dubai institution: an emporium of homemade pastas, freshly baked breads, gourmet fresh and imported treats such as pestos and sweets, and a fromagerie of artisan cheeses. And that's just the deli. The urban chic cafe is not to be missed for breakfast or lunch.

Medley

04 294 1222, pullmanhotels.com

Warm yellow walls enclose beautifully appointed tables with fresh flowers and low lighting. The 'power lunch' at Medley, Sunday to Thursday, is always a hit with diners, who round off an excellent main with a winning dessert and satisfying beverages.

365

04 304 9000, novotel.com

With a handy location between old and new Dubai, at Novotel Dubai Al Barsha on Sheikh Zayed Road, 365 is a no-frills option and a bargain at that. Help yourself to a plate from the buffet and get a drink thrown in for Dhs.65.

Sass Cafe
04 352 7722
Located in financial district DIFC, this swanky evening hangout serves a four-course business lunch that's sure to impress, and is handy for those based in the area. A live pianist keeps the atmosphere mellow.

Switch
04 339 9131, meswitch.com
Light the fires of inspiration by surrounding your team with an innovative decor and funky design. Described by its creator, Karim Rashid, as 'a strong, soft, womb-like space', Switch should nurture creative ideation in your workers; its space age, experimental interior lends a touch of the wow factor to this Dubai Mall outlet.

Tom&Serg
04 338 8934, tomandserg.com
Hip breakfast joint Tom&Serg is buzzing throughout the day with a mix of grungy hipster types, business lunchers and stay at home mums. The utilitarian warehouse setting is softened with quirky touches and a focus on good, tasty food. It's just what Dubai's been missing.

At.mosphere Grill, Dubai

"THE HARD WORK REALLY DOES PAY OFF"

Brett Smyth

Business The Big Chief, EngageME Consulting
Web EngageMEConsulting.com
Activities Communication and engagement solutions in the workplace
Strengths Management consultancy, business, marketing, communications

With a background in management consultancy, Brett Smyth set up EngageME to provide employee communication and engagement solutions. Creativity is at the heart of the company; creating richer conversations, unlocking potential and driving positive transformation in the workplace.

What made you decide to set up your business in the UAE?
The UAE is a hive of activity and opportunity – an exciting place for any budding entrepreneur. I've had a long association with the region and have watched the UAE go from strength to strength each year. But given how quickly the region has grown, and the transient workforce, many companies have invested little in developing an engaged workforce or building a strong corporate culture. There was a very clear need for EngageME's services.

What is your biggest motivation in business?
The penny dropped when I was completing my MBA in London. Many leading business gurus – such as Anita Roddick (Body Shop), Steve Jobs (Apple), Richard Branson (Virgin) – all started their companies with very humble beginnings. It was primarily the ingredients of action, hard work and tenacity that transformed their companies into the successful entities that they are today. I take constant inspiration from this, particularly when the going gets tough. I'm also fortunate to have friends and family who have started their own companies – their support and encouragement motivates me on a daily basis.

Any Advice?
If you really believe in your idea and you've done your research, have the conviction and courage to turn it into reality. Lots of people have great ideas – the difference between an entrepreneur and a dreamer lies in the doing. Enjoy the ride!

What resources did you use during the process of setting up?
It's important to do your homework when setting up in the UAE. There are so many factors to consider, particularly around registration, visas and licensing. It can be a tricky and confusing process to navigate. Fortunately, more and more resources are becoming available – like this publication. The UAE is actively promoting the growth of its business sectors and you will frequently find someone in your network that has started up a company here. Take them out to lunch and pick their brains!

What challenges did you face in setting up in the UAE?

Every entrepreneur, no matter where they set up in the world, faces the typical challenges of securing funding, building a client base and managing their cash flow. In the UAE, there is the added challenge of registration and licensing fees. Before you've earned a dirham, you commit to a considerable outflow of capital. Research as much as possible and do a cost-benefit analysis of all your options. Remember to think beyond year one.

How does the reality differ from expectations?

I've loved every second spent setting up EngageME Consulting. Starting on your own as an entrepreneur is a lifestyle change. Don't make the mistake of assuming it is a way to get rich quick, or a way to escape the eight hour working day. I've never worked so hard in my life and the real benefits will only be seen in the long term. The exciting news is that the UAE is packed with opportunities and the hard work really does pay off.

How has EngageME grown since you started the company?

I've been overwhelmed by the success of EngageME since launching. Our client base continues to grow and that has been matched by the expansion of our EXTRAORDINARY team. It's easy to get swept up in the tide of success and grow too quickly, under-delivering in the process. Don't be afraid to turn client work down if you think you can't deliver at a high quality. We've had to say 'so sorry, we can't help you this month' to a few clients. Fortunately, all have been very understanding and are more than happy to wait to work with us.

How do you switch off from the constant pressure?

That's a tough one! Starting a company is like looking after a baby. At the start, it requires your constant attention, but as it grows, you can slowly step back – a fraction! It's important to find time to relax and refresh otherwise the adventure of starting a business can quickly become stale. I've taken the extreme approach of entering Ironman races to force me to leave my desk in the evening and train. The discipline of exercising actually helps me manage my time and be more productive. I also get all my best ideas when I'm out running, swimming or cycling.

What is the most rewarding thing about seeing your idea turn into reality?

I often have to pinch myself to check that I'm not dreaming when I look at what we've achieved to date. I'm fortunate to have an incredible team – we go all out for our clients and the most rewarding part is when we get great feedback. It makes the long hours all worthwhile.

DON'T MAKE THE MISTAKE OF ASSUMING IT IS A WAY TO GET RICH QUICK, OR A WAY TO ESCAPE THE EIGHT HOUR WORKING DAY. I'VE NEVER WORKED SO HARD IN MY LIFE AND THE REAL BENEFITS WILL ONLY BE SEEN IN THE LONG TERM

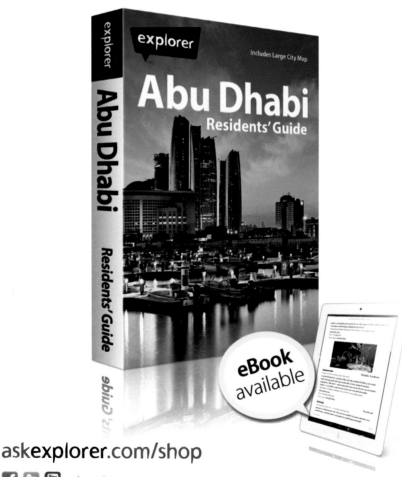

WOMEN IN BUSINESS

HEELS & DEALS   188

HEELS
& DEALS

SOME OF THE MOST INFLUENTIAL EMIRATI WOMEN ARE PROVING THAT WHEN IT COMES TO BUSINESS, THE UAE IS AN OPEN PLAYING FIELD

OF THE WORLD'S
100 MOST
POWERFUL
ARAB WOMEN

23

ARE BASED IN
THE UAE

THE UAE
RANKED
HIGHEST FOR
TREATING
WOMEN WITH
RESPECT

Despite preconceptions we may have of the Middle East, women are rocking the business world in the UAE. As you'll see from the following pages, there are many bright, talented young women in the Emirates taking the leap from a well-paid job with a steady, tax-free salary, to going it alone with a smart idea and a lot of guts.

It's a given that young, career-minded individuals move to and remain in the UAE due to plentiful job opportunities (especially compared to their home country), and fast-tracked career advancement. This positive, optimistic environment is particularly empowering to the women expats that are finding doors thrown open much faster and more abundantly than they may have otherwise encountered.

And as role models go, some of the most influential Emirati women are themselves proving that when it comes to business, the UAE is an open playing field. On Arabian Business's list of the World's 100 Most Powerful Arab Women, there are no less than 23 UAE-based businesswomen – almost a quarter. Topping the list is the UAE's first female cabinet minister, Sheikha Lubna Al Qasimi, whose achievements extend far beyond her role as government minister. The prominent Emirati has a portfolio of successful businesses under her belt including online marketplace Tejari, which she founded in 2000.

The Emirates' unerring support for women filters down from the top. Dubai's forward-thinking ruler HH Sheikh Mohammed bin Rashid Al Maktoum is a strong advocate of female leadership, making concerted and public efforts to push talented women through the ranks. Most notable is the rapid rise of Reem Hashimi, the eloquent Minister of State and the public face of Dubai's successful World Expo 2020 bid.

These barrier-busting women have set the tone for a thriving community of female entrepreneurs.

R.E.S.P.E.C.T

Fundamentally, there is a healthy level of respect for women in the Arab culture of the UAE that we have the country's Islamic heritage to thank. Whatever your thoughts on splitting a bill or keeping up with the boys, there are certain aspects of the local cultural codes that as a woman are worth taking advantage of – ladies-only queues for example! A team of economists at Harvard Business School found that the UAE actually ranked highest of 132 nations studied for treating women with respect in their Social Progress Index.

DUBAI'S FORWARD-THINKING RULER HH SHEIKH MOHAMMED BIN RASHID AL MAKTOUM IS A STRONG ADVOCATE OF FEMALE LEADERSHIP

Business Networks

Most countries have set up business associations in the UAE such as the British Business Group, South African Business Council and Australian Business Council. They all offer excellent networking opportunities and provide valuable knowledge exchange events for women and men alike.

However, there's still a long way to go for women in business. There's a lingering culture of 'old men's clubs' in the UAE, but fewer outlets for women to connect, network, and make an impression. Compared to global figures of 37%, just 2.5% of businesses in the UAE are female-owned, but this figure is rising. Several government initiatives and publications aimed at SMEs and entrepreneurs are worth checking out for opportunities for funding and networking.

Support For Women Entrepreneurs

A number of business networks specifically for women have been cropping up in the UAE. Many are locally-run, while some are branches of more global networks. These are great platforms for women to find support and exchange ideas. Many also organise workshops and events for women to develop their knowledge and skills in all aspects of business.

Dubai Business Women's Council

dbwc.ae

DBWC was established in 2002 by the Dubai Chamber of Commerce and Industry as a platform to encourage women in the business sphere, and create opportunities for and support female entrepreneurs. DBWC runs an annual programme in cooperation with MasterCard called Ro'Ya (meaning dream or vision), in which women can bid for funding for their business concept (or very early stage SME). Keep an eye out on the DBWC website for the next entry opportunities.

International Business Women's Group

ibwgdubai.com, ibwgabudhabi.org

This is another one to look into, with branches in both Dubai and Abu Dhabi. Membership is for 'Decision Makers' – including entrepreneurs, proprietors, partners etc. – provided they are, of course, female. The group organises workshops and networking opportunities.

Heels & Deals

heelsanddeals.org

This is a global network for female entrepreneurs, and holds regular events in Dubai. Membership costs, but if you need inspiration and advice from like-minded women, you might find it here.

Women successfully do business in the UAE

Mompreneurs Middle East

mompreneurs.me

A recent addition to the UAE's female networking landscape is the thriving Mompreneurs Middle East community – a networking platform for UAE business owners who are also mothers. This organisation hosts popular supportive events for commercial mums and counts some of the UAE's most ingenious businesses among its members.

Abu Dhabi Businesswomen Council

adbusinesswomen.ae

This Abu Dhabi organisation provides technical and administrative support to women in business.

Emirates Business Women Council

uaebwc.ae

A UAE-wide organisation, EBWC offers consultancy for female entrepreneurs, with the view of eradicating discrimination.

Sharjah Business Women Council

sbwc.ae

Another opportunity for women to connect, this time in Sharjah, which has a strong history of female empowerment.

"MY BIGGEST MOTIVATION IS THAT I AM A WOMAN"

Born and raised in Brazil, Lilliam graduated in hospitality with a Masters in marketing; a result of her passion for design and pretty things. After purchasing a decal online and seeing how simple they were, she started researching. It snowballed from a hobby alongside her day job into a busy, successful business.

Lilliam Pollard

Business Founder and CEO, E-Walls Studio
Web ewalls-s.com
Activities Design and production of vinyl wall stickers
Strengths Graphic design, branding, marketing, social media, creativity

How long did it take to turn your idea into reality?
I'm self-taught so it was a fairly slow process as I was still working when I set everything up. But it took me over a year to make the big decision of quitting my day job and jumping headfirst into the business. This is possibly the scariest part of it, since you are giving up a steady income.

How did you decide which type of trade licence to get?
It was trial and error. I did a lot of research and went for a free zone licence initially. But, because there isn't a specific section of the activity that I actually do, I received a lot of misinformation. It turned out that because of the service I provide (which includes selling to mainland), I could not trade under a free zone licence. This was a pretty costly mistake, as you don't get refunds. I had to go back to the drawing board and decided to go the Department of Economic Development (DED) mainland route.

What is your biggest motivation as a woman in business?
My biggest motivation is that I am a woman. Men dominate this market. We get very weird looks when women turn up to install a wall sticker. But that sets us apart and that's what drives us to provide a better standard of service. Sorry boys, but there are very few things that I think that women can't do better. We are multitasking queens!

What resources did you use during the process of setting up?
I used Creative Zone to help set up my licence. Even though this whole process was a massive headache, it meant I didn't have to do as much of the footwork in the long run. Plus, they are more up to date with the latest changes on the rules and procedures.

What was your biggest obstacle in setting up in the UAE?
Each step has a hurdle and each one seems to get bigger and bigger but it makes you more efficient. The fit-out and set-up of the office was probably the biggest obstacle though as it's so out of your control. You need so many approvals from so many different governing bodies; it takes a lot of time and a lot of patience. Deep breaths help a lot.

How does the reality of owning and running a business in the UAE differ from expectations?
No matter how much advice you get or research you do, the reality of the start-up process and the day-to-day are very different to any expectations you can have. And while there are no corporate taxes to pay, there are lots of hidden costs that end up burning a hole in your pocket the same way tax does.

How confident are you about the sustainability of your business now it is up and running?
There's a demand for the service I provide, that is evident or we wouldn't still be here four years later. But as this business has grown organically, and with no initial start-up injection, it has taken longer to get there. Financially it makes sense but there's still a long way to go.

How do you switch off from the constant pressure?
I do make an effort to have a life outside work. I didn't used to be able to do that when work was at home, but work stays in the office these days. It's difficult to switch off my phone and I am still online 24 hours, but if you do not take time for yourself, what is the point of working so hard?

Do you think the UAE is a positive place for female entrepreneurs?
The good thing about the UAE is the ladies' queues! And I do think the UAE embraces women entrepreneurs. No one ever says you can't. You do need an NOC from your husband every now and then (as I am still on his visa), which is slightly irritating as it's nothing to do with him – but that's the culture in which we live and we have to respect that. People give us funny looks when women turn up to install a sticker but I find that empowering. Anything a man can do, I can do, but better!

Do you feel it has all been worth it?
Most days. You do get quite a few challenges along the way that make you rethink. But ultimately, I still love what I do and I want to continue doing it. I have big plans and big dreams, so as long as they are alive, I'll keep going!

> SORRY BOYS, BUT THERE ARE VERY FEW THINGS THAT WOMEN CAN'T DO BETTER. WE ARE MULTITASKING QUEENS!

Any Advice?
Speak to people; find out as much information as possible about the process. But go for it; it'll be a long road but it's so worth it. You have to give your dream a chance. Its better to regret something that didn't work out than something that could have been.

"IN MANY REGIONS, BEING A WOMAN CAN WORK TO YOUR ADVANTAGE"

Donna Benton
Business Founder and CEO, The Entertainer
Web theentertainerme.com
Activities Lifestyle incentives
Strengths Recruitment, branding, sales and marketing

Australian entrepreneur Donna Benton founded The Entertainer in 2001 after identifying a gap in the market to provide consumers with dining incentives and enable restaurants to reach new customers. The brand now has a presence across the Middle East and is expanding globally.

What gave you the idea for your business?
I was actually driving down Sheikh Zayed Road (the main highway in Dubai) and I noticed the huge number of restaurants, but there was no incentive for people to take time out of their day and visit a restaurant they've never been to before – and this is how the idea for The Entertainer came to be.

What were the most challenging aspects of starting up?
One of the most challenging aspects is finding the start-up capital, or an investor who believes in your business plan as much as you do. To make it work you have to watch what you spend, so to start I was the only employee in the company. I managed all of the corporate legalities to set the business up, recruited all of the merchants the first year, oversaw the printing and production, admin and finance, negotiated the distribution agreements and did most of the direct sales myself, literally door to door.

Looking back, I treasure this challenging experience as it gave me invaluable insights about starting a business, learning from the mistakes I made along the way and getting to know an industry that I had no previous experience of. Like all entrepreneurs I had to work extra hard to nurture the business through its growing years. I enjoyed it all and I still love what I do today.

What advice would you give to women starting up in the UAE?
I feel that women need to change their own perception of being a woman in business and consider how, in many regions, being a woman can actually work to your advantage. Women are very good at connecting with people and generating trust in what

Any Advice?
My advice to women would be simple – be brave. If you have a good idea for a business, but you're always putting off taking that leap into the unknown, don't be afraid to take some risks and put your fears to one side.

they are creating, so they can often be better at building a business from the ground up. Women are also very good at multitasking so that definitely helps in starting a business.

Starting your own business definitely isn't easy and don't underestimate the work ethic and belief in the product that you need. Remember, you can love what you do, but if the figures don't add up, it'll become more of a hobby rather than a business.

Did you use any support services for women or entrepreneurs? To be honest, no I didn't. I believed in myself, I believed in the product, I knew I had the right work ethic and I just went for it.

How easy/difficult is it for a woman to set up in the UAE? Fortunately the gender gap is closing and more and more women are becoming hugely successful in business across the world. More locally, I feel that the UAE nurtures a strong entrepreneurial spirit and this may be in part due to the lack of discrimination on nationality or gender in dealing with various authorities. As a result, there are a number of great small to medium-sized enterprises in Dubai led by impressive women who are raising the bar for women in business here and continuing to inspire other women to do the same.

THE UAE NURTURES A STRONG ENTREPRENEURIAL SPIRIT AND THIS MAY BE IN PART DUE TO THE LACK OF DISCRIMINATION ON NATIONALITY OR GENDER

The Entertainer

"THERE IS NO SUCH THING AS AN EASY RIDE"

Hazel Jackson founded biz-group with just Dhs.4,500. The business has developed from a small training company to a regional organisation servicing the Middle East's corporate training, team building and strategy needs. It was ranked ninth in the Dubai SME 100 2013.

Hazel Jackson
Business CEO of biz-group
Web biz-group.ae
Activities Coaching, training, team building, business strategy
Strengths Advertising

Any Advice?
Make sure you don't get into debt, the UAE is not an easy place to find funding as an expat, and you risk going to jail if you bounce a cheque. Start small if necessary and self-fund your growth, one step at a time.

When did you found your business?
I started up in 1993, when the systems and processes were very different.

What gave you the idea for your business?
I was visiting to help a client launch a product in the Middle East; at the time, I was working for an advertising agency in London. I found Dubai to be entrepreneurial, but noticed that the levels of sales and customer service were poor. I believed that I could make a difference, so I decided to start a training consultancy business.

What were the most challenging aspects of starting up your own business?
I didn't really know anything about the training business, plus I only had Dhs.4,500 to my name, so it was a steep learning curve and a lot of hard work in the early days. Fortunately, I wasn't afraid of either and used to spend hours on the phone making appointments, and even more time drinking masala tea as I talked to senior managers (HR wasn't really strong then) about their business needs and challenges with people.

What advice would you give to women starting up their own businesses in the UAE?
First, be really passionate about the business you want to run as there is no such thing as an easy ride. A lot of potential clients in the early days will give you positive feedback about your business idea, but that doesn't mean they are going to spend money. If you're passionate this will help you continue when times are tough.

biz-group in action

Did you use any support services for women or entrepreneurs? Back in the early 1990s I used more of an informal network of advisors, but the best support group came when I'd grown my business to just $1million in revenue and I was introduced to the Entrepreneurs Organisation (EO), Dubai Chapter. This is a global group of 8,000+ entrepreneurs, not at the early start-up stage, but at the scale-up stage in business. They have some great networks, safe forum discussions and amazing learning opportunities. Being part of EO helped me grow my business, and myself, significantly. They now have an Accelerator Programme to help start-up companies as well. In addition to networking and groups, I read a lot of business books.

How easy/difficult is it for a woman to set up in the UAE? It is easy for either gender to start a business in the UAE, but it isn't necessarily easy to succeed. For women, if you have the support of a spouse, it can make the first few months and years easier from a financial perspective. However, this can also be too much of a comfort zone and could mean you don't need to succeed.

The UAE is a great place to start and run a business, as long as it is something you are truly passionate about and prepared to work really hard at.

THE UAE IS A GREAT PLACE TO START AND RUN A BUSINESS, AS LONG AS IT IS SOMETHING YOU ARE TRULY PASSIONATE ABOUT AND PREPARED TO WORK REALLY HARD AT

"NETWORK. LIKE YOUR BUSINESS DEPENDS ON IT. BECAUSE IT DOES"

Dawn was born in Ireland but has lived in England, France, Spain, Japan, Thailand and China. She arrived in Dubai in 2008 and isn't leaving any time soon. Her first book, Managing the Matrix, came out this year in English and the Arabic version is due shortly.

Dawn Metcalfe
Business Managing Director, Performance Development Services
Web performancedevelopmentservices.com
Activities Executive coaching, mentoring, facilitation
Strengths Speaking plain English and playing fair

When did you found your business?
I came to the UAE in 2008 and set up my company in 2010. It was scary as we were still in the middle of the recession, but I am delighted I did it.

What were the most challenging aspects of starting up your own business?
Suddenly not having anyone else to go to was the most challenging thing at the start, although also the most exhilarating. As we grow it's about giving up some control – that's never easy!

How long did it take you to turn your idea into reality?
In some ways it was immediate – the first time somebody hired me was the idea being turned into reality. And in some ways it never ends, as every single step since has felt like a step into another reality: the first repeat client, the first referral, the first hire, the first book coming out, the first overseas partner and so on.

Any Advice?
Do it. Don't think too much and just do it. If you can do it as a 'hobby' or side-job first to learn about the market, that's even better. But don't spend too much time planning – you'll never know if it will work for sure until you do it.

What advice would you give to women starting up their own businesses in the UAE?
Make sure you have what I call a 'brain trust', or people you trust to be on your side to answer your questions. And network. Like your business depends on it. Because it does.

Did you use any support services for women or entrepreneurs?
I didn't attend anything specific to women – but I did rely heavily on the free zone and the Irish Business Network at first. For women-only services I'd recommend 85 Broads and Reach, the mentoring programme for women, as great places to start.

How difficult is it for a woman to set up in the UAE?
Not difficult at all. I've been treated as well as a man in every situation I can think of. And on a few occasions being a woman helped as I was able to skip the queue.

How confident are you about the sustainability of your business?
It depends what day you ask. As I write this the business is in better shape than ever – we have loyal customers, a great team and our clients work as our advocates. I feel blessed. On the other hand, you're only ever as good as the last thing people remember about you, so we work hard to make sure we keep our clients happy – that's the route to sustainability for my business.

How do you switch off from the constant pressure?
What pressures? I have been described as 'one of those annoying people who really enjoys their work' and that means that the work isn't pressure at all. Running a business is different of course, but I have a great team of people who make my life very easy and I also have a home from home in Sri Lanka where I have two dogs and 14 parakeets. I do work there but it's a very different environment. In fact, we're starting a creativity workshop there later this year.

I'VE BEEN TREATED AS WELL AS A MAN IN EVERY SITUATION I CAN THINK OF. AND ON A FEW OCCASIONS BEING A WOMAN HELPED AS I WAS ABLE TO SKIP THE QUEUE

Networking pays off

MOMPRENEURS

Who says women can't have it all? When it comes to business, here's why mother knows best.

There's a new generation of entrepreneurial mothers – 'mompreneurs' – filling gaps in the UAE business market and building successful companies. There is a fine art to balancing motherhood and business, but there is a noticeable increase in the number of stay-at-home mums taking the risk and banking on a small business idea.

In the UAE, businesses that range from party supplies to fitness studios, business support services to event planning, are being run by women with a child or two in tow. Mompreneurs Middle East is a platform for these business-minded mothers to connect.

Managing director of Decluttr Me, a service for organising and decluttering homes and offices, Shelina Jokhiya finds networking vital to her business.

Shelina Jokhiya
Business **Decluttr Me**
Web **decluttrme.com**

What gave you the idea for your business?
I nurtured the idea for over 10 years with a friend. We thought it would be great to utilise our organisation skills but never thought it could be a business until I started Googling and discovered it was a big industry.

What challenges did you face when setting up?
There was a lack of understanding of the concept, which resulted in me having to educate people first before I could start providing the services. I attended a lot of networking events, posted on various social media forums and asked my friends to spread the business name through word of mouth.

How has Momprenuers Middle East supported your business?
They have given me the opportunity to become part of their network. We are also working together to provide decluttering and organising advice for the mompreneurs.

Can you recommend any other support organisations?
I belong to BNI – Falcon's Chapter (bni.com). BNI is a great networking venture which works on the basis that the group members pass referrals and refer each other's business to third parties. By passing referrals from trusted sources we are making sure we can get quality business.

Julie Leblan
Business **My List**
Web **MyList.ae**

CEO and founder of MyList.ae, the first online gift registry in the Middle East for weddings, baby showers and group gifts, Julie Leblan tells us about the challenges she faced setting up her business.

Any Advice?

Having your own company is the best way to have enough flexibility to be with your children (especially when they are very young). Try to separate your personal life from your work life; your personal life is sometimes quite challenging but it does not mean that you can work any less.

What gave you the idea for your business?
I arrived in Dubai when I was six months pregnant and with a 16-month-old son in late 2010, and launched my online gift registry company by the end of 2011. Previously a finance solicitor, I set up MyList.ae after struggling to find a way for my friends and family in Europe to send my baby shower gifts.

What challenges did you face when setting up your business?
It was a challenge to get information from banks, the licensing office and others. I had to experience everything myself, talk to a lot of people, and it was difficult back in 2011 to find the right information. I spoke with fellow entrepreneurs and received a lot of support from the French Business Council.

How has Mompreneurs Middle East supported your business?
Mompreneurs Middle East offers many services to help create your own company and expand your business. It's a great network with lots of organised events, where you can interact with other mompreneurs and professionals from various industries. It also organises very affordable training sessions on a variety of topics, and is a useful, accessible online platform.

Can you recommend any support organisations?
Mompreneurs Middle East, of course! I have also created a women's business club within the French Business Council (FBC) known as Women in Network by FBC, and I am also a member of the Dubai Business Women's Council.

"EXPAT MUMS DO NOT HAVE THE SUPPORT OF THEIR FAMILY"

Mona Tavassoli

Business Momsouq
Web Momsouq.com
Activities Online community for mothers
Strengths Marketing, tourism strategy, serial entrepreneurship

Mona Tavassoli is founder and CEO of Momsouq.com, an online community for mums in the UAE launched in 2012. Mona also set up Mompreneurs Middle East, a B2B platform for female entrepreneurs to connect with each other, share expertise, advice, recommendations and contacts.

Tell us a bit about your company Momsouq.com...
The website has different sections, such as: Classifieds for parents to buy and sell their items; Expert Corner to read about various topics; Inspirational Moms; and many more. We also organise events every month for families and mums.

What gave you the idea for Momsouq.com?
My son was the inspiration behind Momsouq. As a new mother, I realised that there is a need for parents to buy and sell their kids' items, especially when they are still babies and they outgrow their toys and clothes very quickly. In addition, it's very common to receive duplicate gifts. That is essentially how I came up with the idea.

What challenges did you face when setting up?
I was lucky as we already had another business running and I could use the resources of our online advertising agency. We went through a lot of red tape to establish our first business and it was quite costly to get a licence and rent an office from the beginning. It was also challenging to spread the word without any marketing budget. We used our network and social media to send the message out.

How has Momsouq.com grown and expanded since you started the company?
We always add new sections and features to the website as per the market's demand. We also started various events to meet our community and engage with them. In addition, we have launched a new website for Mom Entrepreneurs called Mompreneurs Middle East.

Any Advice?

Use your network as the most powerful marketing tool is word of mouth. And it's okay to ask for help, we don't need to do everything on our own. Ask for help from your husband, family and friends.

As the founder of Mompreneurs Middle East, can you tell us how this group came into being?
After launching Momsouq in March 2012, I got to know many other mums who set up their own businesses and had the same challenges of marketing them. We started promoting the mums on our social media channels initially, and by September 2012 there were 25 companies that we were promoting for free. We added a section on the website to promote their business and today we have around 200 companies registered on there – mainly from the UAE, but also from other countries too.

What is the main aim of Mompreneurs Middle East?
We are a B2B platform for mum entrepreneurs to promote their businesses, connect with each other and also attend networking and training sessions every month. We also provide them with special discounts and services through our strategic partners.

How do you see Mompreneurs expanding in the coming years?
We are aiming to expand to other countries and make it easier for our community to meet entrepreneurs from across the region and also globally. We are also partnering with other organisations to offer more workshops and mentoring sessions.

Do UAE mums face different challenges to global mothers?
The majority of the UAE mums that we work with are expats, and they do not have the support of their family when they run their businesses. Being an entrepreneur gives the flexibility to manage and balance time; however, having your own business is very demanding, especially in the first couple of years.

What are the greatest challenges of being a mompreneur?
I am lucky that my business involves kids and mums, therefore my son comes to the office with me from time to time; I have the flexibility to spend time with my son. It is very easy to go off balance and I keep reminding myself about my priorities. It is important not to forget other areas of life.

What personal tips do you have for aspiring mompreneurs?
I recommend spending some time doing activities that are for yourself only. It is very important to take care of your wellbeing, it has a direct effect on your family and business.

Can you recommend any support organisations?
I highly recommend Dubai Business Women's Council. Right Selection brings international speakers to the region and their events have helped me to work on the fundamentals of my business. biz-group also provides great training sessions.

> BEING AN ENTREPRENEUR GIVES THE FLEXIBILITY TO MANAGE AND BALANCE TIME; HOWEVER, HAVING YOUR OWN BUSINESS IS VERY DEMANDING, ESPECIALLY IN THE FIRST COUPLE OF YEARS

"NEVER BE AFRAID TO ASK QUESTIONS"

Annabelle Fitzsimmons
Business Co-founder, LittleMajlis.com
Web LittleMajlis.com
Activities e-commerce, online marketplace
Strengths design, creativity

Annabelle Fitzsimmons co-founded Little Majlis in 2012 with business partner Anna Bolton-Riley. The site is a boutique shopping destination for unique products that are not otherwise readily available in the market. It has grown into an online community for UAE-based artisans and craft fans.

What gave you the idea for your business?
The artisan marketplace concept is not a new one, but it was new to the region when we launched. We were inspired by the amazing underground arts and crafts scene that was developing in the Emirates at the time and wanted to give these creative people a legal platform to showcase and promote their work.

Our focus is on locally made items from the Gulf, but we accept products from other regions too, provided that they're unusual and exceptional in terms of quality, workmanship and creativity.

Did you face any challenges when setting up your business? How did you overcome them?
Little Majlis is self-funded and getting the initial set-up off the ground was a massive hurdle for us. The big-ticket items included the trade licence, legal consulting, a hefty security deposit for the payment gateway and appointing a web developer to build the site.

Our next major challenge was stocking up the marketplace and developing a customer base. Unlike regular e-commerce websites, we rely completely on our shopkeepers to list their products for sale and fill the shelves of the Little Majlis market. It took a good six months for the market to look full and varied enough for customers to feel they could have a good shop.

Traditional advertising is incredibly expensive and we've had to be creative when it comes to marketing and spreading the word about Little Majlis.

Any Advice?
Working for yourself does not mean that you'll be working less; so having a passion for what you do is essential.

Do you have any advice for aspiring mompreneurs?
Never be afraid to ask questions because the SME community is surprisingly embracing and willing to help out, which has saved us a lot of time and money along the way.

How has Mompreneurs Middle East supported your business?
Mompreneurs Middle East has been brilliant in helping to spread the word about Little Majlis and we were introduced to some of our shopkeepers at their events. We attend the Mompreneur Meetups as often as possible. The atmosphere is welcoming, the speakers are relevant and always informative and these events attract a group of like-minded women. We've found networking with people who are facing the same issues as us to be really beneficial.

Can you recommend any support organisations/networks for entrepreneurs?
There's a great entrepreneurial spirit here in the Emirates and we've found people to be incredibly generous in offering advice and support. We attend networking and mentoring events whenever possible and our recommendation is to try out a few groups and see which is the best fit for you. Meetup.com is a great place to start your search.

THERE'S A GREAT ENTREPRENEURIAL SPIRIT HERE IN THE EMIRATES AND WE'VE FOUND PEOPLE TO BE INCREDIBLY GENEROUS IN OFFERING ADVICE AND SUPPORT

DIRECTORY

Embassies & Consulates

UAE

Australia	04 508 7100
Bahrain	02 665 7500
Canada	04 404 8444
China	04 394 4733
Czech Republic	02 678 2800
Denmark	04 348 0877
Egypt	04 397 1122
France	04 408 4900
Germany	04 349 8888
India	04 397 1222
Iran	04 344 4717
Ireland	02 495 8200
Italy	04 331 4167
Japan	04 331 9191
Jordan	04 397 0500
Kuwait	04 397 8000
Lebanon	04 397 7450
Malaysia	04 398 5843
Mexico	02 558 0088
The Netherlands	04 440 7600
New Zealand	04 331 7500
Norway	04 382 3880
Oman	04 397 1000
Pakistan	04 397 0412
Philippines	04 220 7100
Qatar	04 396 0444
Russia	04 328 5347
Saudi Arabia	04 397 9777
South Africa	04 397 5222
Spain	02 626 9544
Sri Lanka	04 398 6535
Sweden	02 417 8800
Switzerland	04 329 0999
Thailand	04 348 9550
UK	04 309 4444
USA	04 309 4000

Government Departments & Offices

Abu Dhabi

Abu Dhabi Central Post Office

PO Box	11
Call Centre	600 5 99999
Location	Sultan Bin Zayed The First St, Al Danah
Timings	Sat-Thurs, 7.30am-9pm
Web	epg.gov.ae

Abu Dhabi Chamber of Commerce & Industry (ADCCI)

PO Box	662
Tel	02 621 4000
Fax	02 621 5867
Location	Corniche West St, Markaziya West
Timings	Sun-Thurs, 8am-3pm
Web	abudhabichamber.ae

Abu Dhabi Courts

PO Box	84
Tel	800 2353
Location	Al Khaleej Al Arabi St
Timings	Sun-Thurs, 8am-3pm (Registration) Sun-Thurs, 7.30am-7pm (Declaration)
Web	adjd.gov.ae

Abu Dhabi Water & Electricity Authority (ADWEA)

PO Box	6120
Tel	02 694 3333 Fax 02 694 3192
Location	Fatima Bint Mubarak St, Al Dhafrah
Timings	Sun-Thurs, 7.30am-2pm
Web	adwea.ae

Abu Dhabi Municipality (ADM)

PO Box	263
Tel	02 678 8888 Fax 02 677 4919
Location	Sheikh Zayed Bin Sultan St
Timings	Sun-Weds, 7.30am-5pm Thurs, 7.30am-3.30pm
Web	adm.gov.ae

Department of Economic Development (DED)

PO Box	12
Tel	02 815 8888 Fax 02 672 7749
Location	Baniyas Towers, Al Danah
Timings	Sun-Thurs, 7.30am-3.30pm
Web	ded.abudhabi.ae

Emirates Identity Authority (EIDA)

Tel	600 530 003
Location	Nr Mazyad Mall, Tower 3, Mohamed Bin Zayed City
Timings	Sun-Thurs, 7.30am-8pm
Web	emiratesid.gov.ae

General Directorate Of Residency & Foreigners Affairs (GDRFA)

PO Box	4333
Tel	02 446 2244 Fax 02 446 1621
Hotline	6005 22222
Location	Al Saada Rd, Al Mushrif
Timings	Sun-Thurs, 9.00am-7.30pm
Web	adnrd.ae

Ministry of Economy

PO Box	901
Tel	02 613 1111 Fax 02 626 0000
Location	Hamdan Bin Mohammed St, Al Danah
Timings	Sun-Thurs, 7.30am-2.30pm
Web	economy.ae

Ministry of Foreign Affairs

PO Box	3785
Tel	02 222 2000 Fax 02 222 2000
Location	Al Bateen
Timings	Sun-Thurs, 9am-4pm
Web	mofa.gov.ae

Ministry of Labour

PO Box	809
Tel	04 702 3333 Fax 02 449 4293
Location	Baynounah St, Al Bateen
Timings	Sun-Thurs, 8am-7pm
Web	mol.gov.ae

Dubai

Department of Economic Development (DED)

PO Box	13223
Tel	04 445 5555 Fax 04 445 5991
Location	Business Village, Port Saeed
Timings	Sun-Thurs, 7.30am-1.30pm
Web	dubaided.gov.ae

Dubai Central Post Office

PO Box	111311
Call Centre	600 5 99999
Location	Al Karama
Timings	Sat-Thurs, 7.30am-9pm; Fri, 3pm-9pm
Web	epg.gov.ae

Dubai Chamber of Commerce & Industry (DCCI)

PO Box	1457
Tel	04 228 0000
Call Centre	800 2426237
Fax	04 202 8888
Location	Baniyas Rd, Riggat Al Buteen
Timings	Sun-Thurs, 8am-4pm; Sat, 8am-1pm
Web	dubaichamber.ae

Dubai Courts

PO Box	4700
Tel	04 334 7777 Fax 04 334 4477
Location	Riyadh St, Umm Hurair 2
Timings	Sun-Thurs, 8am-3pm (Registration) Sun-Thurs, 7.30pm-7pm (Declaration)
Web	dubaicourts.gov.ae

Dubai Electricity & Water Authority (DEWA)

PO Box	564
Tel	04 601 9999 Fax 04 601 9995
Location	Nr Wafi Mall, Umm Hurair 2
Timings	Sun-Thurs, 7.30am-2.30pm
Web	dewa.gov.ae

DIRECTORY

Dubai Land Department
PO Box	1166
Tel	600 555 556 Fax 04 222 2251
Location	Baniyas Rd, Riggat Al Buteen
Timings	Sun-Thurs, 7.30am-2.30pm
Web	dubailand.gov.ae

Dubai Municipality (DM)
PO Box	67
Tel	04 221 5555, 800 900
Fax	04 224 6666
Location	20 Baniyas Rd, Al Rigga
Timings	Sun-Thurs, 7.30am-2.30pm
Web	dm.gov.ae

Emirates Identity Authority (EIDA)
Tel	04 383 2333, 600 530 003
Location	Dubai Central Post Office, Al Karama
Timings	Sun-Thurs, 7.30am-8pm
Web	id.gov.ae

General Directorate of Residency & Foreigners Affairs (GDRFA)
PO Box	4333
Tel	04 313 9999 Fax 04 501 1111
Hotline	800 5111
Location	Nr Bur Dubai Police Station, Al Jafiliya
Timings	Sun-Thurs, 8am-8pm
Web	dnrd.ae

Ministry of Economy
PO Box	3625
Tel	04 314 1555 Fax 04 358 1811
Location	Etisalat Bldg, Al Kifaf
Timings	Sun-Thurs, 7.30am-2pm
Web	economy.gov.ae

Ministry of Foreign Affairs
PO Box	3785
Tel	04 404 0014 Fax 04 357 2112
Location	Khalid Bin Al Waleed St, Umm Hurair 1
Web	mofa.gov.ae

Ministry of Health
PO Box	1853
Tel	04 230 1000, 800 1111
Fax	04 230 1988
Location	Nr Etisalat Academy, Muhaisnah 2
Timings	Sun-Thurs, 8.30am-2pm
Web	moh.gov.ae

Ministry of Labour
PO Box	5025
Tel	04 702 3333 Fax 04 261 6114
Location	Al Doha St, Al Qusais 1
Timings	Sun-Thurs, 8am-7pm
Web	mol.gov.ae

Ministry of Labour: Tas'heel
PO Box	215262
Tel	04 404 0404
Location	Business Venue Bldg, Oud Metha
Timings	Sat-Thurs, 7.30am-8pm
Web	tasheel.ae

Northern Emirates
Fujairah Court 09 222 2111
Sharjah Court 06 502 4100, *justice.gov.ae*
Ajman Chamber of Commerce and Industry 600 595 959, *ajmanchamber.ae*
Fujairah Chamber of Commerce 09 222 2400, *fujcci.ae*
Sharjah Chamber of Commerce & Industry 06 530 2222, *sharjah.gov.ae*
Chamber of Commerce & Industry of Umm Al Quwain 06 765 1111, uaqcci.ae
Ras Al Khaimah Chamber of Commerce & Industry 07 207 0222, rakchamber.ae
Sharjah Electricity & Water Authority 06 528 8888, *sewa.gov.ae*

UAE
du 800 155, *du.ae*
Etisalat 800 101, *etisalat.ae*
Federal Electricity and Water Authority 06 711 1111, *fewa.gov.ae*
Federation of UAE Chambers of Commerce & Industry 02 621 4144, *fcciuae.ae*

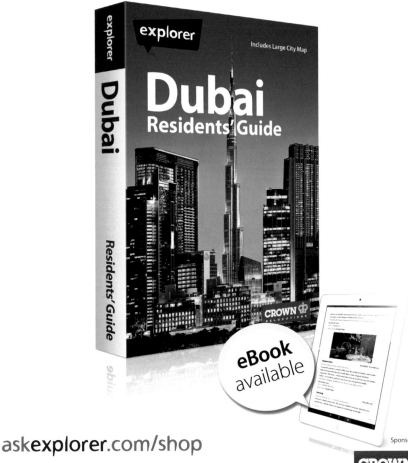

INDEX

NOTES

Explorer Products

Residents' Guides

Visitors' Guides

Photography Books & Calendars

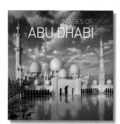   

Check out ask**explorer**.com

Maps

Adventure & Lifestyle Guides

Apps & eBooks

+ Also available as applications. Visit askexplorer.com/apps.

* Now available in eBook format.

Visit askexplorer.com/shop

UAE Business Guide – 1st Edition

Lead Editor Lily Lawes
Written by Mark Atkinson, Alicia Buller, Andy Mills
Contributors Donna Benton, Annabelle Fitzsimmons, Dina Ghandour, Jalel Ghayaza, Hazel Jackson, Shelina Jokhiya, Shailaja Khan, Julie Leblan, Jamie Liddington, Dawn Metcalfe, Lilliam Pollard, Samer Qudah, Peter Shaw-Smith, Brett Smyth, John Martin St. Valery, Mona Tavassoli, Simon Whittle, Colliers International, Hadef & Partners
Proofread by Kara Martin
Data managed by Mimi Stankova
Designed by Ieyad Charaf, Jayde Fernandes, M. Shakkeer

Publishing
Chief Content Officer & Founder Alistair MacKenzie

Editorial
Managing Editor Carli Allan
Editors Lisa Crowther, Lily Lawes, Kirsty Tuxford
Research Manager Mimi Stankova
Researchers Amrit Raj, Roja P, Praseena, Shalu Sukumar, Maria Luisa Reyes, Lara Santizo, Jayleen Aguinaldo, Jacqueline Reyes

Design & Photography
Art Director Ieyad Charaf
Designer M. Shakkeer, Mohamed Abdo
Junior Designer Niyasuthin Batcha
Layout Manager Jayde Fernandes
Cartography Manager Zain Madathil
Cartographers Noushad Madathil, Dhanya Nellikkunnummal, Ramla Kambravan, Jithesh Kalathingal
GIS Analysts Aslam, Jobydas KD
Photographer & Image Editor Hardy Mendrofa

Sales & Marketing
Director of Sales Peter Saxby
Media Sales Area Managers Laura Zuffa, Sabrina Ahmed, Bryan Anes, Simon Reddy, Sean Rutherford
Digital Sales Manager Rola Touffaha
Business Development Manager Pouneh Hafizi
Director of Retail Ivan Rodrigues
Retail Sales Coordinator Michelle Mascarenhas
Retail Sales Area Supervisors Ahmed Mainodin, Firos Khan
Retail Sales Merchandisers Johny Mathew, Shan Kumar, Mehmood Ullah
Retail Sales Drivers Shabsir Madathil, Nimicias Arachchige
Warehouse Assistant Mohamed Haji, Jithinraj M

Finance, HR & Administration
Accountant Cherry Enriquez
Accounts Assistants Sunil Suvarna, Jayleen Aguinaldo
Administrative Assistant Joy H. San Buenaventura
Reception Jayfee Manseguiao
Public Relations Officer Rafi Jamal
Office Assistant Shafeer Ahamed
Office Manager – India Jithesh Kalathingal

IT & Digital Solutions
Web Developer Mirza Ali Nasrullah, Waqas Razzaq
HTML/UI Developer Naveed Ahmed
IT Manager R. Ajay
Database Programmer Pradeep T.P.

Contact Us

General Enquiries
We'd love to hear your thoughts and answer any questions you have about this book or any other Explorer product. Contact us at **info@askexplorer.com**

Careers
If you fancy yourself as an Explorer, send your CV (stating the position you're interested in) to **jobs@askexplorer.com**

Contract Publishing
For enquiries about Explorer's Contract Publishing arm and design services contact **contracts@askexplorer.com**

Retail Sales
Our products are available in most good bookshops as well as online at askexplorer.com/shop or Amazon. **retail@askexplorer.com**

PR & Marketing
For PR and marketing enquiries contact **marketing@askexplorer.com**

Corporate Sales & Licensing
For bulk sales and customisation options, as well as licensing of this book or any Explorer product, contact **sales@askexplorer.com**

Advertising & Sponsorship
For advertising and sponsorship, contact **sales@askexplorer.com**

Explorer Publishing & Distribution
PO Box 34275, Dubai, United Arab Emirates
askexplorer.com

Phone: +971 (0)4 340 8805
Fax: +971 (0)4 340 8806